Casa Z~
Pleas.   ve
C000185489

A SPANISH
TAPESTRY

Copyright © Jill Newman-Rogers 2013

Published by Acorn Independent Press Ltd, 2013.

The right of Jill Newman-Rogers to be identified as the Author of the Work has been asserted by her in accordance with the Copyright, Designs and Patents Act 1988.

This book is sold subject to the condition it shall not, by way of trade or otherwise be circulated in any form or by any means, electronic or otherwise without the publisher's prior consent.

Cecil Day-Lewis quote on page 7 reproduced with the kind permission of the Estate of C Day-Lewis.

ISBN 978-1-909121-33-1

www.acornindependentpress.com

ABOUT THE AUTHOR

Jill Newman-Rogers was born in 1941 into war-torn England. Aged 20, following three years of studies in Paris and inspired by books about the romance and dangers of Spain, she embarked on a riding holiday through Andalusia.

Some ten years later, due to her illicit liaison with a married bullfight impresario, she and her young children were expelled from Spain under General Franco's strict morality laws. Following the dictator's death she was able to return and now lives permanently in Andalusia where she helps to run a charity for abandoned and ill-treated horses.

CONTENTS

A SPANISH TAPESTRY

A journey of legend, history and love

PROLOGUE

My journey takes place in the year 1962, twenty-three years after the end of the Spanish Civil War, when Spain was still in the grip of General Franco's dictatorship. At that time, very few books had been written on the civil war. Only a few foreign authors dared to risk the wrath of the all-powerful Generalissimo Franco by appearing to criticize his dictatorship. Only Spanish authors living in exile could publish comments on the conflict or aftermath without being immediately arrested.

As a result of this rigid censorship, when I arrived in Spain I really didn't know what to expect – perhaps something between groups of dark haired beauties in flamenco dresses on the arms of handsome bullfighters, or starving mutilated peasants tugging at my skirts, asking for food. What I found was a mixture of the two – more starving peasants perhaps than the flamenco dresses.

Today, I do not presume to be an expert on the conflict; there are authors such as Paul Preston who are far better qualified to write on the subject. My only objective in writing this prologue is to give readers a very brief resume of the situation in Spain post civil war, and to offer some insight into the country and its people in those years. The conflict had an enormous impact on the country. Why did people not talk about it? Why was it called "the war that never was"? Why was there still an air of fear? Were General Franco's spies really watching and listening?

In 1936 Spain was a legally elected republic. Reforms were underway, the country enjoyed unprecedented freedom and women even had the right to vote. But infighting in the Republican ranks due to different ideologies and objectives caused general unrest and set

1

the scene for an uprising by right-wing army generals led by General Franco. His self-image was of a benevolent dictator combined with an absolute monarch, leading the Spanish people into righteousness under the Catholic Church. However, in reality, he achieved a death toll of over 500,000.

It was, in essence, a war of ideals, between the haves and have-nots, the rich and the poor, and one war that was not caused by religious beliefs, albeit the church did side with the rebel nationalists. Author Gerald Brenan, in *The Spanish Labyrinth*, described the Spanish political scene as only consisting of two parties, "those who eat and those who don't". At risk of over-simplification, the "rich" were the rebel Francoist supporters(right-wing traditionalists), and the "poor" were the republicans (left-wing liberals and communists).

There were many contributing causes of the uprising: political infighting; the great divide between rich and poor; the abuse of the farm labourers, particularly in the south; the abolition of the monarchy; an unwieldy, powerful army with too many officers; the industrial depression; and, above all, the desire for social change. Spain had always been a predominantly agricultural country and most of the land was owned by some fifty thousand wealthy landowners, "*terratenientes*". But the agricultural community rose up against the great landowners, occupying their lands and killing many of them. In Ronda, several landowners were thrown to their deaths in the gorge by hungry farm workers

Evil Cardinal Goma described the war as "A fight between Spain and anti-Spain, religion and atheism, Christian civilization and barbarism". General Franco himself defended the conflict as "A triumph of light over darkness, truth over error, health over sickness."

Overview

Despite their differences the members of the ruling Republican Party were united in their hatred of the rebel nationalists. The clergy were seen as supporting Franco's nationalist side, which gave rise to violence against them and the inexcusable destruction of churches and their contents. The "reds", as the republicans were known, were dogged in their persecution of religious orders and clergy: in the early years of the war many hundreds of convents and churches were burned, and thousands of the clergy assassinated.

The main protagonists in the conflict were:

NATIONALISTS (THE REBELS)

Most of the Spanish army led by General Franco
The Spanish army in Morocco including the Arab Brigades
The Spanish Fascist party
The Spanish Civil Guard
The Catholic Church
Italy and Germany (both Fascist countries) who supplied troops
and arms

REPUBLICANS (THE DEMOCRATICALLY ELECTED GOVERNMENT)

The Popular Front
The Communist party
The Anarchists
The International Brigades

Communist Russia supplied arms. The French and the British sat on the fence, whilst in theory backing the democratic Republicans, but alarmed by Communist Russian support.

With the total breakdown of civil discipline the infamous *checas* – centres of torture and summary thirty-minute trials – were set up in 1936 by the Republicans. Those judged "guilty" were often told they had been freed and could return to their homes, only to be shot by the militia on their way out of the prison. In all, personnel from ten other countries became involved. The support from Italy, Germany, and Russia changed the balance of power and if it had not been for their interference, the conflict might well have ended differently.

The International Brigades, made up of nationals of many and diverse countries such as Hungary, Finland and Canada, supplied much of the medical personnel, crucial to the troops on the battlefields. A number of young English intellectuals died or were wounded there. The majority of the British who fought in the war sought social change and therefore supported the republic. Over 13,000 foreigners took part in the fighting in 1936. Many of those who came to fight in Spain did so from a conviction that this was the beginning of a greater European conflict, and that by helping the side of republican democracy in Spain they might in some way help mould the futures of their own countries. The foreign powers involved found Spain a useful testing ground for weapons and armies destined to be used within a few years in the Second World War. Spain's struggle became known as the "first battle of the Second World War".

The International Brigaders experienced bodies piled high in the village streets, and set on fire with gasoline; flies; rivers full of corpses; endless diarrhoea; and little food. They were ill-equipped and, in the main, totally unprepared for the type of warfare they encountered. Used by the commanders as cannon fodder, their weapons were antiquated and unserviceable. George Orwell became disillusioned by the war. He was wounded on the Aragon front, but returned home mainly because he was sick of what he saw as the betrayal and political cynicism of the republican coalition.

Orwell tells of the "complete lack of war material".

> The badness of our weapons was so astonishing that it is worth recording. The majority of the rifles were scrap iron, the ammunition was so scarce that each man entering the line was only issued with fifty rounds. We had no tin hats, no bayonets and hardly any revolvers or pistols and not more than one bomb between five or ten men. You greased your rifle with olive oil.

He recounts the problems with illiterate conscripts, who didn't understand the passwords, resulting in several near misses due to the confusion.

Towns were occupied first by one army, then by the opposing troops. Villages and towns were split into two; their inhabitants confused as to where their loyalties lay, or pragmatic, and picking the army which would provide food next winter. Father and son found themselves on different sides of the struggle. Old scores were settled. Men were denounced and shot, their death fuelled by the assassin's greed for their lands or their horses.

At the beginning of the war, even the paramilitary police force, the feared *Guardia Civil*, were split in their ideology. The rich sent their gold outside Spain. The professional classes fled, as did the artists and writers. Spain was plunged into economic disaster. The republican government sent the gold reserves to Russia for safekeeping, and exchanged it for tanks. However, the Russian government would only hand over the tanks to the communist faction within the Republican army. The local communist commanders grew more powerful with this advantage and assumed a greater control of the army. This development alienated England and France who were worried by the increase in Communism on their doorsteps, and the closeness of Spanish relations with Russia. They froze Republican bank accounts in London and Paris, sat on the fence and did nothing to help. The squabbling amongst the different republican factions increased and several historians determine this as one of the main reasons for the failure of the republican army to put an end to the conflict.

A large proportion of the population was illiterate, and many towns found themselves on one side or the other solely because of a geographical accident. The north was mainly a rebel nationalist zone and the south was loyal to the republic. Málaga, though not particularly communist, was dubbed "red Málaga".

Even though the hostilities officially ended in 1939, guerrilla warfare continued across the countryside until 1950. For the "conquered" it was a life of misery, hunger, and fear. The clergy would denounce republicans and have them detained. Forced labour gangs were "rehabilitated" by hard work. The conquered could not mourn their dead, and graves were concealed. No lists of the "glorious dead" included any republican names – they had just disappeared, to be mourned and remembered in secret.

The Long-Lasting Effects
"We have not achieved peace but we have achieved victory."
– General Franco

Between 1936 and 1940, over 500,000 people perished. Of these, 25,000 died from malnutrition. 75,000 were executed by Franco's nationalists and 55,000 were shot by the republicans. 200,000 died in combat and 10,000 in air raids. After hostilities ceased with the overthrow of the republic and the election of General Franco as head of state in the spring of 1939, his troops executed 100,000 republican prisoners and a further 35,000 died in concentration camps. A large number of republican prisoners were sent to Nazi concentration camps and upwards of 10,000 died there. Fleeing republican refugees were interned in French concentration camps on the beaches where they perished, ravaged by illness.

The well-known Spanish poet Miguel Hernandez died alone three years after the end of the war, still a prisoner in an Alicante prison. He had been condemned to death for his poems but his sentence was commuted to life imprisonment. On the wall of his cell he wrote:

> Goodbye, brothers, comrades, friends,
> Say farewell for me to the sun and the wheat.

More than sixty years later his family are still campaigning for his name to be cleared.

Manuel Cortes, the republican mayor of the small village of Mijas near Málaga, and a barber by profession, disappeared towards the end of the war. His wife, Juliana, wore mourning clothes and it was commonly believed that he had been killed. However, after a general amnesty, he reappeared. He had spent thirty years hiding in a secret room in his house, cared for by his wife and daughter without the knowledge of the rest of his family.

Franco's aim was to keep the reign of terror alive in order to control the population, and to maintain the distance between the conquerors and the conquered. When hostilities were over, he had plenty of time to search out those who had opposed him and have them eliminated. Whilst the republicans were responsible for many thousands of deaths, particularly at the beginning of the conflict, the atrocities carried out by Franco's Spanish Foreign Legion and the feared mercenaries of the Arab division left towns with blood running in the streets as thousands of the townspeople were gunned down. Their bodies were left as a warning to anyone who might have harboured republican sympathies. In 1936, in the town of Badajoz, the victorious nationalists shot 1800 republicans in the bullring in cold blood.

In the village of Ubrique, near Ronda, one weeping man told of the sadism of his father's death at the hands of the nationalists from their own village.

They shot him in both legs so he was forced to kneel, then they cut out his tongue. They sent for the village pig castrator and castrated him

He also recounted the death of a young girl, shot when eight months pregnant. The child in her womb was still jerking when the mother was dead.

The attack on the refugees on the Málaga-Almería Road, perpetrated by Franco's nationalist allies, was infamous in its brutality, even by civil war standards. On 8th February l939, Málaga was overrun by 25,000 Italian, German and Moorish troops. The story is told in detail by Norman Bethune, a Canadian doctor who was a member of the Canadian Communist Party and a pioneer in blood transfusions. He invented the world's first mobile medical unit, which was designed to be carried by one mule, and contained blood supplies for 100 operations to be carried out at the front.

On 10th February, with two colleagues, he was driving an ambulance loaded with blood to be used in the treatment of casualties of war in Málaga. They were heading west from Almería towards

Málaga. One hundred and fifty thousand refugees were fleeing along the same road in the opposite direction, east towards Almería, two hundred kilometres away. They were bombarded from the air and sea by planes, submarines, and warships as they struggled along the narrow road, hedged in by the Sierra Nevada on one side, and the beach on the other. There was no other escape route. Dr Bethune describes it as "the greatest and most terrible evacuation of a city in modern times". They travelled on foot: men, women, children and the elderly. They had no shoes and few clothes. Some had a pony or a donkey on which were loaded their few possessions. Their feet were bleeding; they had no food or water.

The doctor counted more than five thousand children under ten years old. Eighty-eight kilometres from Almería, Bethune decided to abandon his journey and for three days they rescued thirty or forty people at a time, making trips to the hospital in Almería, not even pausing to sleep or eat. But the suffering of the refugees was not to end there. On 12th February, when the little port in Almería was full to capacity with exhausted people, the Italian and German planes bombed the town.

Dr Bethune is adamant that the planes were not aiming at the enemy warships in the harbour but deliberately bombing the areas where the refugees were sleeping. He recalls the terrible cry of "intolerable intensity" that arose in the darkness from the desperation of the families, and the macabre scene of death and destruction lit up by the flames of the buildings on fire.

He asked himself what crime this defenceless civil population had committed to be murdered in such a bloody manner. Their only crime, he concluded, was to have voted for a moderate government.

Why did they not stay in Málaga and await the arrival of the nationalists? The families knew their fate if they stayed – all men and boys between 15 and 60 would immediately have been shot.

Future British poet Laureate, Cecil Day-Lewis, wrote of the International Brigades:

> It was not fraud or foolishness,
> Glory revenge or pay,

We came because our open eyes
Could see no other way.

The war ended with the victory of Franco's troops, but the reprisals continued for many years. It has taken more than seventy years for him to be declared guilty of crimes against humanity, and for the investigation into the hundreds, perhaps thousands, of mass graves to begin.

CHAPTER ONE

Life Before Nanny Elsie

"It is only with hindsight that you realise what your childhood was really like." – Maya Lin

I wasn't a bad child – strong willed and rebellious maybe, but not bad. I confess I did ask God to arrange for Nanny Elsie to die, but my prayers fell on deaf ears.

Those of us who spent their early childhood in Britain in the war years became accustomed to hardship and fear. I remember the screech of the sirens as my mother hustled me into the air raid shelter in the cellar of my maternal grandparents' house. Sometimes we spent whole days and nights there – the ground shook as the bombings and the roar of the pilotless planes refused to stop. Arabella, my rag doll, and I huddled together under the blankets and I told her stories so she wouldn't be afraid. It was cold – so cold. During daylight hours there was no gas or electricity. My mother and I made friends with the nice man at the gas works. There was no coal so sometimes he gave us a sack of coke for the boiler, which we pushed home in my pushchair. There were no toys, no treats and little food. But I had known no other way of life.

We were evacuated from war-torn Croydon in 1943 and stayed with my father's parents in Devonshire. Grandpa used to be a tea planter in Ceylon. He was called "Himself", had a bristly moustache, smelled of pipe smoke, and jiggled me on his lap. I hated it and wriggled free. I don't think he liked me very much. He mercilessly bullied Grandma and for some reason called her "Madre", until she finally passed away with cancer. How vivid some childhood memories are.

When I was five we returned to Croydon and my father finally came home from the war. My mother hired a car and we drove to London, to Victoria Station, to meet him. I had only seen photographs of him before, but now he was real and I didn't like him. When my mother cried with happiness, I thought she was crying because she didn't like him either and I told him to go away. He upset our cosy life and my mother seemed not to love me any more. I took my revenge on him by throwing a tin can at his head. I was a good shot even at an early age and he bled copiously and satisfactorily. He didn't hit me or shout. He just stood, blood dripping down his face, and looked at me with infinite sadness.

We continued to live at my maternal grandparents' rather grand Victorian house in Croydon , as my father's strength slowly returned after the terrible deprivations he had experienced in the jungles of Burma. He suffered recurring bouts of malaria.

Granny continued to make jams and potions in her still room. I picked tomatoes in the warm greenhouses, fragrant and deliciously sweet. My mother sent me to collect the eggs and the chickens mounted vicious attacks on my ankles. The dislike was mutual. The windows that had been blown in by the force of the bombs were replaced. The Irish maids contrived secretly to give me biscuits or fruit from their rations. The butler polished the silver serving dishes as though the war had never happened. Then my father was offered the posting he wanted – to be an instructor in jungle warfare at the prestigious Staff College in Camberley.

So I grew up as an army brat, constantly moving house in post-war Britain, as my father took posting after posting. Life at the Staff College was idyllic for children. Officers' families lived in rows of wooden bungalows. Most instructors had young families, and there were plenty of children to play with. Heating was limited to one paraffin stove in the hallway, and I recall breaking off the icicles that had formed on the wall above my bed on winter mornings. Rationing meant few treats but we didn't miss what we had never known. Nanny of the day allowed us to roam unrestricted in the beautiful College grounds, and Mother was only too happy to have us out of her hair. I am sure she loved us but she just wasn't cut out to deal with us without a Nanny to help. In her memoirs she agrees that she could not cope with her children.

Then a new Nanny came into our lives and everything changed.

CHAPTER TWO

Nanny Elsie

With the benefit of hindsight I know that it was the arrival of Nanny Elsie that aroused in me a deep desire for freedom. She was the latest in a long line of genteel ladies employed by my mother to instil discipline in her three children. She proved to be an enthusiast for corporal punishment and, as the oldest of the three, then aged 8, I fared the worst. Beatings were the order of the day and I spent many hours locked in my room. Subjected to a myriad of petty controls, I was constantly in trouble for something. I recall spending a whole day at the dining room table with a sausage in front of me. I was incapable of swallowing the large lumps of gristle some enterprising butcher had camouflaged as meat.

"Do you know how many ration tickets that sausage cost? Most children would be only too pleased to eat it?" she reprimanded me. In those post-war days of food rationing, adults were only allowed one egg, 100 grams of bacon and sixpence-worth of meat per week. This would consist of one can of fish, meat or corned beef. Sausages were like gold dust, but were filled with any leftover bits of meat.

Even my father sympathised as the hours passed, but Nanny reigned supreme. I stayed put until I ate it. When I was left alone I contrived to hide the offending pieces of gristle around the room, under cushions and behind the curtains.

I was not allowed to leave the house without Nanny, classmates were not allowed to visit the house and nor could I go to birthday parties. School trips to museums or theatres were forbidden and requests for clean underwear denied. Even toilet visits were to take place at times to suit Nanny or, a smacking followed. All trivial enough, but I was deeply unhappy. My classmates jeered "She needs a nanny, how feeble is that? She's not even allowed to come to the cinema. Nanny won't let her."

Rebellion and rudeness achieved nothing but more punishment. The worse my behaviour, the wider the smug smile of satisfaction on Nanny Elsie's face. Over the next few years I dealt with my frustration by reading. We had moved to a large Victorian monstrosity of a house in Sussex when my father left the army. I had discovered a room full of musty books that nobody seemed to read. There were no children's books so I devoured tales of travel, adventure, death and romance, and classics written by adventurers – Rudyard Kipling, John Buchan, Washington Irving and Richard Ford or soldiers such as Napoleon and Wellington. In particular, it was the books written by travellers in Spain that I soaked up like a sponge.

In the nineteenth and early twentieth centuries the "romantic" travellers threw caution to the wind and travelled through Spain in search of new experiences. Thomas McGann, an American, wrote "Spain is romantic – battles, bulls and flamenco dancers, but also dirt, cruelty, arrogance and the inability to be on time".

George Orwell saw "white mountains, the dungeons of the Inquisition, Moorish palaces, mule trains snaking their way up the mountains, grey olive and lemon groves, young women in black mantillas, Málaga wines, cathedrals, cardinals, bullfights and serenades."

I dreamed of the beauty and romance described with such passion by these intrepid wanderers. When things got tough they seized every opportunity for adventure, almost inviting danger.

There was no adventure in my life. Nanny Elsie didn't allow me to go to the shops or the library. But I had my own library – my own heroes and villains – in the magical room of books.

I read by torchlight under the covers, terrified that if she discovered the pleasure my books gave me she would immediately have them locked away.

Every night, for years, before sleep overcame me, I prayed, "Please let Nanny Elsie die, and make it soon."

***

One fateful day, believing that I had completely concealed myself in the branches of the rhododendron bush, I settled down to a quick private voodoo session. Suddenly a hand grabbed my arm,

"What are you doing with that doll and why are pins sticking out of it?

Nanny grabbed the small rag doll I had made and foolishly written 'Nanny' on its head, with incriminating pins sticking out of its eyes.

"You're hurting my arm. Let go. I hate you, hate you and I hope the evil spirits will kill you."

"You are the evil one, you're wicked and you'll be punished. You just wait and see what your parents make of this."

I tried to escape but she had me firmly by the arm, and once again I was locked in my bedroom. Taking my scissors from their hiding place, I scratched yet another date on the wooden bed head – another day of punishment.

Next morning my mother summoned me.

"Nanny is very upset; whatever possessed you to act like that? She has threatened to leave and I can't face looking after you three without her. I need her, so your father and I have decided it's *you* who must go. You're going to study in Paris. You're sixteen – quite old enough. We're leaving on Friday."

I alternated between elation and terror. So controlled had my childhood been that I doubted my ability to fend for myself. Paris – such a romantic city. But how would I manage on my own? I hardly spoke French. Perhaps I should apologise to Nanny? No, that just was not an option. Should I appeal to my father? No, he would take the easy way out and side with my mother. Oh, my god, I had really burned my boats. That night I cried myself to sleep.

Next morning I decided I had to get a grip. But I had no experience of life away from home. All I had to draw on was the characters in the books I had read. What would they have done? Washington Irving or Richard Ford wouldn't have given up. At last here was my chance to live in a world without Nanny. Wasn't freedom what I wanted? It seemed that despite my prayers she wouldn't die, so I had to get away from her.

Five days later I was delivered, like a parcel, to Madame Labouret in Avenue Victor Hugo. "It's for the best," my mother assured me as she climbed into her waiting taxi.

My journey to independence and freedom had begun. Aged only sixteen I had been launched into a new language, a new country, and a new life.

CHAPTER THREE

Paris

"Anyone who stops learning is old, whether at twenty or eighty." – Henry Ford

Paris was scary. Life swirled around me at a dizzying speed: wide boulevards; crowded pavement cafés; the fast flowing river; and the magnificent tranquillity of the Cathedral of Notre Dame, which became my refuge when tears of loneliness overtook me; and of course the aromas of stale garlic, Gauloises and fresh bread.

I studied literature and philosophy at the Sorbonne and absorbed the writings of French poets and novelists. I discovered French authors who were also fascinated by the romance of Spain, such as Baron D'Avillier, who wrote of his travels through Spain on horseback in the late nineteenth century. His books were illustrated by the great artist Gustave Doré.

Théophile Gautier was another French author who found the danger of Spanish travel by coach appealing. He spoke of the "peril that encircles you, follows you, goes before you, is all around you".

The Latin Quarter teemed with student life, of which I soon became a part. Thousands of students jostled in and out of classes and I gloried in the feeling of being part of the vibrant crowd. I became accustomed to being groped on the Metro by hairy, garlic-breathed workmen and became adept at retaliating with a sharp elbow to the solar plexus, or a sharp stamp on the offender's foot. The Labouret household was comfortable, except for the continual advances from the adolescent son, Thierry, who assumed that *la petite anglaise* had been imported solely for his pleasure. My bedroom door didn't have a lock. I ensured that I was never home alone with him.

I did, however, meet Anthony, a fellow English student. Unlike the smooth Mediterranean-skinned Parisians, he was afflicted with bad Anglo-Saxon acne. My French hosts sneered behind his back when he came to the door to take me out. But, acne or not, he introduced me to the pleasures of heavy petting, and proved to be an entertaining escort. His weekly allowance from his parents was generous so he paid for our entertainment and we agreed that I would repay him one day when I was rich and famous.

I lived my student life to the full, glorying in the freedom I had so craved. Jazz sessions in dark smoke-filled cellars, stimulating lectures and endless sessions in cafés discussing religion, sex, and philosophy. Our tutors encouraged us to investigate, to debate, to be curious about life, and, above all, to read. Never had I been so happy.

Good looking, young Jesuit priests were very much in evidence in the university. Their mission to save our souls and train us to embrace Catholicism proved a difficult one. Our cosmopolitan group was bent on enjoying all that their student existence had to offer, and was not too interested in religion. Despite this, we were encouraged to join in Catholic seminars and pilgrimages. I was cajoled into one such walk which took us from Paris to Chartres Cathedral – a long way with unsuitable footwear. My blisters and sunburn interfered with any attempt at meditation and I contracted viral foot and mouth disease from cleaning my teeth alongside a large brown cow in a water trough. The sound of several thousand students chanting in unison with the bearded priests as we walked was stirring, but my reading had convinced me that religion was at the root of most conflicts, so I wasn't an easy convert.

Each Sunday I met up with a small group of friends and we set the world to rights over a glass of wine and a cheese omelette at a small café overlooking the river.

***

Three years later, my parents no longer wanted to foot the bill for my student life and I needed to find a job which allowed me time to complete my studies. Now, aged nineteen, I took a live-in position with Barbara Bray, the Paris correspondent for the *Observer* newspaper, and a writer for the BBC. She was a widow with two little girls, who I was to care for. At the time, I had no idea how well-known my employer was. In one obituary she was described as "one of the most significant links between English and French literature in the twentieth century". Samuel Beckett was a frequent visitor to the apartment. He was a tall, craggy, distant man who seemed to fill the small apartment with his rather intimidating presence. He seldom spoke more than two words to me and I was encouraged to make myself and the two little girls scarce, during the many hours that they spent closeted in her study. Barbara's intelligence was, it appears, a magnet to him, and he consulted her about his work. Although married to Suzanne, who he had met when they fought in the French Resistance together against the Nazis, Barbara was his main mistress and intellectual soul mate. Known to be a womanizer, he is said to have regarded sex as no more important than a good meal. Both Suzanne and Barbara tolerated his many sexual encounters, and his discreet relationship with Barbara lasted until his death.

A year later, I had passed my exams with flying colours and was the proud owner of a certificate stating that I had obtained a degree in French Literature and Psychology. The rather cushy job with the Bray household came to an end, as they temporarily moved to London. My need to earn a living found me back in England in the only accommodation I could afford – a small bedsitter in Notting Hill Gate. What a come-down from romantic Paris. The bedsitter was cold and the gas meter ate shillings. It rained endlessly, as I trudged the streets and visited employment agencies. The building where I lived was mainly occupied by Nigerian students and the shared kitchen and bathroom were unsanitary and smelled of African spices. But funds were short and I couldn't afford anything more upmarket. At least I could spend weekends at my parents' house in Sussex, although Nanny Elsie was still in residence. It seemed that my mother still needed her support though only my brother, now aged 14, was still at home in his school holidays. He had been packed off to boarding school where he was deeply unhappy.

A friend introduced me to Ron Hubbard, the founder of the Church of Scientology, and he persuaded me to join their ranks. An ex-science fiction writer, he was famous for the comment: "If a man really wants to make a million dollars, the best way would be to start his own religion."

It seemed he had done just that. But I was prepared to try anything new to liven up my tedious and impecunious existence in London. Perhaps the concept of "freeing my soul by wisdom and thus clearing my mind" might be positive? We learned that "Scientology is here to rescue you", but that "God helps those helps themselves". Seemingly contradictory. But the endless study sessions, some taught by the great man himself, were confusing. Accustomed as I was to my studies in Paris, where human psychology was analysed and discussed in great depth, Scientology's teachings seemed inconsistent and muddled. My "inappropriate behaviour" was criticized. I could not afford the endless demands for financial donations for the greater good of the Church. Probably the fact that I was permanently hungry had something to do with my lack of enthusiasm. My small salary, as a temporary secretary, just covered my rent, the gas meter, and a permanent diet of cheap cabbage, boiled, fried or in soup, didn't help my concentration.

At this time, my relationship with my current boyfriend, pipe-smoking Keith, was not progressing well. Scientology played a large part in his life and my lack of enthusiasm for it was causing some friction between us.

"If I get naked and put on this rubber mackintosh and you take your clothes off and pretend to be my mother, we could have sex on the floor?", he proposed, one rainy afternoon. Not a very romantic start for my first sexual encounter. Perhaps it was part of the Scientology search for spiritual awareness? I looked round at the grubby threadbare carpet and the sad bearded figure in his mackintosh, then turned and beat a hasty retreat. The smell of stale cabbage seemed to follow me down the steps as I fled from Keith and Scientology.

Next there was Michael – he was clean-cut and good looking and the type my parents would have approved of. Above all, he was normal, and not into mackintoshes or rubber gloves. He was also funny, considerate with my lack of experience in bed, and above all, earned more money than I did. We dined out on pizza and pasta and I never touched cabbage again. He didn't thrill me or move mountains, but we were friends. There was one problem in our relationship: Michael was a cycling champion. One evening a week was dedicated to waxing his legs, two to training and for three days before a race, sex and alcohol were out of the question as his trainer deemed it debilitating. We parted good friends when it became clear that his bicycle was winning the race for his affections.

One day I was leafing through a copy of *The Lady*, that British magazine which is so evocative of the slightly faded and distressed aristocracy. Ladies of a certain age advertised their services as discreet companions to elderly parents and the family Labrador and educated young ladies were sought by well-to-do families to care for their children. I was desperately looking for any excuse to leave damp, grey, dull England again. Surely my expensive education must have prepared me for a more challenging life than my new job as a secretary in the basement office of a London ready-mix cement distributor.

A small advertisement caught my eye: "Alondra Riding Parties". Small groups of horse lovers were invited to join these parties in the Andalucían village of Álora in Spain. The villages along the way would be those visited by the intrepid travellers in search of adventure a century before and on the route of the bandits. We were to be housed in the home of a Spanish marquis. The cost in the month of August was less than thirty pounds for two weeks. My horse-loving godmother had left me one hundred pounds in her will and what better way to spend her legacy? I knew she would have approved. The heat would be gruelling in August and I still had to get to Andalucía, but I immediately seized the opportunity and booked a fourteen-day holiday.

CHAPTER FOUR

The Romantic Travellers

"Everything is so well arranged, so admirably combined, so plainly labelled that chance is an utter impossibility. If we go on progressing in this fashion towards perfection for another century, every man will be able to foresee everything that will happen to him from the day of his birth to the day of his death. Human will will be completely annihilated. An intense feeling of ennui will then take possession of the globe for the principal spring of life, namely curiosity, will have been destroyed for ever." – Théophile Gautier

While France and Italy were much visited by the early travellers on the *Gran Tour* of Europe and considered an essential part of a young gentleman's education, Spain was inaccessible and different. The inhospitable terrain, lack of acceptable transport, bandits and reportedly appalling food deterred all but the most intrepid. However, the tales of bullfights, duels, bandits, gypsies and flamenco proved irresistible to many romantics, as well as myself.

I spent all my spare time in the next weeks in the library researching all I could on Spain, determined to be prepared for this, my Spanish adventure. I reread writings by some old favourite nineteenth and early twentieth century travellers such as Richard Ford, Laurie Lee, Théophile Gautier, Washington Irving, and discovered some new books by the likes of the evangelical missionary George Borrow, who travelled the country on his Arab horse Sidi Habismilk,

Enthusiasm for horseback travel and bandit encounters produced a plethora of books and despite the hardships they reported, nothing could dampen my enthusiasm. No sooner had these travellers set foot in the door of their *posada* (a humble Spanish inn for travellers and their horses) than they put pen to paper to record their experiences.

A.C. Andros concludes that:

> Spain has great advantages like a splendid climate, fine paintings, lovely women, gorgeous Moslem and Gothic relics, picturesque scenery and mournful traces of ancient grandeur. Yet when I reflect on the poverty-stricken nature of the country, its ignorance, its tardy advance in civilization, its bigotry and religious intolerance, the inferior quality of the hotels, the nasty style of living, the vermin, the garlic, the oil and the smells, I exclaim... Thank God I am an Englishman!

During the nineteenth century the English were some of the most intrepid visitors to Spain and, due to the ease of travel by ship to Gibraltar, (only six days from Southampton) it became fashionable to travel what became known as the *Ruta de los Ingleses,* the Route of the English. After disembarking in Gibraltar the journey would take them on horse, mule or by horse-drawn coach through Algeciras, following the ancient rocky routes used by bandits and smugglers, to Gaucin and the inhospitable mountains of Ronda. The road had not been repaired since the end of the War of Independence, to deter the smugglers who used the route. Many of the visitors were military personnel stationed in Gibraltar. Tired of the claustrophobic Rock, they sought adventure in Spain. I planned to travel through France and northern Spain. I was still debating how to travel to Andalucia as the train and bus were expensive.

Many travellers that made it to Spain came from countries such as France and England which were so "domesticated" that they felt their art was unable to flourish. Bored with their everyday routine, they searched for something different and I sympathised with that notion only too well. Franz Borkenau, an Austrian Jew, wrote in 1937

> Life (in Spain) is not yet efficient, not mechanized, beauty is still more important for the Spaniard than action, honour is often more important than success, and love and friendship are more important than work.

Spain was different and, like a lamp, attracted the motley horde of romantic travellers like a cloud of moths.

My reading led me into the world of the dark and sometimes violent world of the bandit. The bandits and smugglers were idealized by these "romantic travellers", such as the young Disraeli, who were secretly captivated by the idea of being held up by a handsome highwayman. What a story to tell on their return, embellished by accounts of their own bravery in the face of violence. It was essential that the bandit be a gentleman and cause them no bodily harm. Being held up by a common thief or footpad was not on their agenda. Author William Clark recalls that "The first question a traveller will be asked on his return from Spain is – have you encountered a bandit?"

Unfortunately for the lady travellers, it appears that few of the bandits were even passably good-looking, but I was still hopeful.

Richard Ford wrote to the British Ambassador in Madrid advising him to buy a cheap watch before embarking on his journey, to appease any thieves who might stop him. Benjamin Disraeli travelled to cure his depression with his boring life and lamented the lack of bandits. He always carried sixteen dollars, the minimum he considered a suitable offering to a bandit to avoid being shot.

Baron D'Avillier lamented

> Alas, we have never seen, far or near, the figure of a single brigand, although we have frequently traversed

the roads and rocky defiles recommended as the most likely and dangerous. We had not the good fortune to encounter a single armed adventurer, which is much to be regretted, as a few words from the lips of a living bandit would have greatly enlivened our narrative.

I was determined to retrace the steps of these romantic travellers in their search for adventure, even if the bandits were now in short supply.

CHAPTER FIVE

The Train from Madrid

"The English have more money than they know what to do with and on that account they wander all over the world, paying dearly for what no other people care a groat for." – George Borrow

To my parents concern, I decided to save money and hitchhike through France to pick up the train in Madrid. My near perfect command of the French language stood me in good stead and the journey was uneventful if uncomfortable. Long distance lorries aren't built for comfort, and the enormous potholes in the Spanish roads left me bruised and battered. The drivers accepted my rejections of their unwelcome sexual advances with good grace, and I never felt myself to be in any danger.

I heaved a sigh of relief when we finally reached Madrid.

The *coche correo*, the coal-fired mail train from Madrid to Málaga, was due to leave the romantic glass-domed station of Atocha at four p.m. The earlier train was more expensive, being slightly faster, and a ticket on the express train was a luxury I could not afford. However, on the positive side, I would have many hours to practise speaking Spanish and I had at least been understood so far. According to the timetable, the journey was to take a day and a half, plus any delays from breakdowns and problems along the way, such as livestock on the line. I planned to make a stop in Córdoba, the city that had played such a large part in the history of Spain, and to continue to Málaga the following day.

The train groaned and rattled its way south through the parched and dusty plains of central Spain, making frequent stops to deposit hot and weary passengers at tiny stations along the way. Sometimes only one small whitewashed house was visible when the train stopped, an impenetrable hedge of prickly pear cactus marking its boundary. The barking of a tethered hunting dog would herald the arrival of the train, the only excitement of the day in the searing heat and monotony of an Andalucían summer. Stout-aproned ladies manned the level crossings, their naked, swarthy children crowding round their skirts as they waved at the passing train.

For the first few hours after we left Madrid my fellow passengers were mainly country women, returning home from the market laden with baskets, and mysterious items wrapped in striped blue-and-white linen bundles. Terrified hens stuck their heads out of baskets from whence issued a cacophony of protests, and rabbits were stowed unceremoniously in boxes on the luggage racks. The passengers chattered shrilly, remonstrated with fractious children and stared unashamedly at me – the only foreigner, and the only lone traveller. I knew they were all sizing me up and wondering if I was Swedish.

In the repressed post-war era of Andalusia the first groups of Swedish tourists had arrived on the Costa del Sol, with their reputation for skimpy bathing suits and loose morals. There had been reports of girls wearing bikinis, although the *Guardia Civil* frowned on this semi-nudity and reprimanded the offenders. Posters were placed on the beaches prohibiting the wearing of bathing costumes, let alone bikinis, except whilst bathing. Once out of the water it was mandatory to cover up.

In 1953, the mayor of Benidorm, threatened by the archbishop with excommunication, finally tired of interference in the affairs of his town. He set off on his motorbike, five hundred kilometres to Madrid, to consult with the dictator, General Franco, on the vexed subject of bikinis. He had an eye to developing tourism in his town and was clashing with both the Catholic authorities and the green-clad gun-toting *Guardia Civil* on the subject the invasion of semi-naked females on the beach. After an expensive civil war, the Generalissimo desperately needed foreign currency. Whilst he would be in trouble with his wife, Doña Carmen, a very religious woman, and indeed would alienate the all-powerful Catholic Church, it took little to convince him that encouraging tourists by permitting bikinis would help solve his currency problem. So it was official – the bikini was here to stay and the mayor returned triumphant to Benidorm.

Having lived a free and liberal life in Paris, I was unsure what would await me in Spain. In 1962, the church and state, in unison, maintained an iron grip on the country, acting as self-appointed guardians of the country's morals. The liberties permitted by the republic, prior to the civil war, were abolished. Civil marriages and divorces were annulled, causing heartbreak and hardship as those who had divorced were obliged to return to their previous spouses, who had frequently remarried. Couples who had entered into a civil marriage and had children, now found that their marriage was cancelled and that they were living in sin with illegitimate children. Homes purchased by married couples were now owned by two people who were possibly now married to others. Widows lost their pensions, and children lost their inheritances. Abortions were prohibited and unmarried couples were forbidden any form of physical contact in the street. The husband's permission was required for most of his wife's activities, such as opening a bank account, buying a house, or indeed any travel, and she had little freedom of choice on any important matters. The title deeds for house purchases needed to state that a married woman had her husband's permission to sign the documents, even if the funds belonged to her.

Under the new order there was a purge of the vanquished Republicans from the educational system. Six thousand teachers were shot and more than seven thousand imprisoned. Marxists, Jews and freemasons were eliminated or fled.

Higher education was almost impossible for women and their role was that of mother and homemaker. Prizes were given by the government for large families. Homosexuality and lesbianism were now crimes against the state. The press and radio were censored and on Sundays, and during Easter week, only holy music was permitted on the radio.

Into this environment of repression and state control came the planeloads of *suecas* – Swedish female tourists – arriving on the coasts, and bringing a breath of fresh air. However, away from the coastal resorts, attitudes had not relaxed.

So it's no surprise a young British woman travelling alone in the spirit of Lady Louisa Tenison, caught the disapproving eye of the travellers in the carriage. Such things were unheard of in inland Spain.

Accustomed to the freedom of my student existence in Paris, Spain was very surprisingly different.

"I am *inglesa*," I explained to my fellow travellers, English not Swedish, but foreign was foreign and they still regarded me with suspicion. It was clear that, in their opinion, I obviously suffered from severe moral laxity travelling, as I was, without a chaperone or a parent. Their dark-eyed children stuck out their tongues at me behind their mothers' backs, their thighs red with welts from the uncomfortable wooden slats of the seats.

Our conversation was laborious as my Spanish was still pretty basic, but I struggled on. My fellow passengers were fascinated and somewhat scandalized that I dared to make my journey with no member of my family, or at least a friend.

"How come you are alone? Where are your parents?"

"What if you are robbed?"

But I was relaxed – hadn't I read somewhere that robbery is the exception rather than the rule in Spain?

"I plan to travel on horseback to Ronda" I searched for the right words, "on the mule tracks that the bandits used. I'm going to retrace the steps of the romantic travellers and perhaps meet up with a bandit or two."

Blank faces digested this information and I thought they had misunderstood my Spanish. Until one by one they burst into laughter.

"You are mad, girl. You, a lone blonde foreigner. Will you ride side-saddle? You can't mean to wear trousers?"

Embarrassed by their laughter, I retired into my corner. It was too hot for this interrogation. "No I am not Swedish, and no I am not married. I'm only twenty," I snapped.

"What madness!" Who would want to risk being kidnapped by a bandit or a smuggler? Dismissing such outrageous thoughts, they returned to their gossiping. One by one they arrived at their stops, heaved baskets of animals, bundles, and children to the ground, and set off for home.

The engine frequently spat out prodigious puffs of smoke and showers of black soot that made it essential to close the windows. This had to be done with care as the windows acted like a guillotine, severely damaging the fingers of the unwary as they wrestled with the recalcitrant latches. With the windows closed, the heat was stifling.

Spanish rail travel was still in its infancy in 1962, largely due to the difficult nature of the terrain and the inhospitable and, until recently, bandit-infested mountain passes. Trains were infrequent and usually late and, to quote a frustrated Augustus Hare, move "at the speed of old mule traffic – at a plod". In the words of Walter Starkie, an Irishman who worked the Spanish trains with his guitar, "the trains crawl like camels". He told of blind beggars who invaded the carriages and a cripple who had lost both legs and was carried round on a tray. The Duke of Wellington objected to the railways on the basis that "it would encourage the lower classes to move about" and another traveller described the ancient carriages as "rabbit hutches on wheels". I kept reminding myself that this was an adventure and that several of the earlier women travellers journeyed this route on horseback. I at least had the luxury of a seat on a train, however uncomfortable.

The sun beat down on my dilapidated wooden third-class carriage encased in green tin, with its running board like a vintage car. The tin casing transformed it into an oven in the August temperature of over 43 degrees centigrade. The only way of changing carriages was to wait for a station and run along the platform to the next door, as there was no connecting corridor. The ticket collector performed acrobatic feats on the footboard, changing carriages with the train in motion. The windows were tiny and designed to keep the sun out.

The cramped, slatted pine seats became purgatory after only a few miles, and I envied the larger *señoras* their ample buttocks. Second-class had enviably soft, grey seats and the first-class carriages were furnished in walnut, with comfortable seats and carpeted floors similar to the Orient Express.

I pretended to sleep to avoid further questions, however well-meaning. I must have dropped off, lulled by the creaking of the train, as I awoke suddenly, sweating with fear, from a nightmare of Nanny in which she cackled demoniacally with a mouthful of black teeth, and chased me down the train track. I had escaped from her clutches, but still she haunted me.

No food or drink was available during the journey; however the stops at the major stations were always long enough to allow passengers to descend to stretch their legs and buy refreshments at the station stalls. The guard would call out on arrival at the larger stations, "*Veinte minutos!*" – twenty minutes to buy our snacks.

I had read about these hurried stops from a nineteenth century traveller, Italian novelist Edmondo de Amicis, who wrote of his surprise at a small Spanish station when he descended from the train in search of food. By the time he managed to push his way through the crowd to enter the restaurant, fifty of his fellow passengers were already seated, stuffing their mouths with desperation whilst the waiters, bathed in sweat, raced about "like exhausted horses", spilling soup and sauces. The proprietor of the establishment was frantic. When the bell rang to signal the departure of the train "devilish confusion" reigned. The waiters pursued those who had left without paying and those who wanted to pay couldn't find a waiter. The station master shouted "*Aprisa*," hurry up, and blew his whistle.

I just boarded the train in time.

The smaller stations had no stalls or restaurants, but most of the travellers had come prepared with food, *tortillas*, omelettes filled with potatoes and onions, – rough crusty bread, luscious purple figs, home-made goats' cheese, all carried in small wicker baskets covered with a snowy white cloth. Blue-black blood sausage from Ronda, *morcilla*, made with onions and rice and fragrant with cloves, cumin and garlic, and *salchichón*, spicy pork sausages with peppercorns, were sliced with wicked-looking pocket knives.

Unaware that the train had no cafeteria, I had embarked on the journey without provisions. With customary Spanish hospitality, my companions were quick to offer to share their food and brushed off my thanks. I was overwhelmed with gifts of more food than I could hope to eat and embarrassed to refuse their generosity. However little they had, they insisted on sharing it with me and I was touched by their generosity.

At every small station the women and children water-carriers would be waiting with their big earthenware water jugs. Heads would erupt from the train windows at the cry of *agua fresca*, cool water. A refreshing tin mug only cost a few cents, and was very tempting after hours in a sweltering tin carriage. Beggars, musicians and terribly mutilated civil war veterans worked the carriages, begging for a coin to buy food.

Little fried birds lay in baskets, beaks gaping in their last agony, ready to be consumed with relish in one crunchy mouthful by my fellow passengers. Baskets of toasted almonds appeared as if by magic, hoisted up to the carriage windows. Knife-sellers and watermelon vendors roamed the platforms, and a good trade was done by ladies selling cooked shrimps from brimming baskets. The aroma of rotting shrimp shells lining the floor of the compartment added a new dimension to the stench of garlic and the food detritus trampled underfoot.

The trains' plumbing was primitive a hole in the floor with footprints either side. The smell was unmentionable. There was a small basin with a tap but no water.

It was adventure I had wanted and it looked like adventure I was going to get.

CHAPTER SIX

Ana and Maria

"It seemed as if the air had fainted and the pulse of nature had run down and ceased to beat."
– Unknown traveller

Ana and Maria were travelling from Madrid to Córdoba. They were both dressed entirely in black, which made them look older than their thirty-or-so years. In Andalucía it was the custom to remain in deep mourning for the rest of one's life if the deceased was close family. It was acceptable to progress gradually to dark grey clothing after some years, if the deceased was a more distant relation. As Laurie Lee observed, since the Spanish Civil War, "Spain is a country of widows". During the war years, General Franco's troops forbade women to wear black or to show any sign of mourning for their murdered husbands and families.

The ladies told me that they were returning from visiting family in Madrid. They chattered ceaselessly, outdoing each other in volume. Apparently it made no difference that neither paid any attention to the other. Legs akimbo in their ample black skirts, continually tugging at their *corses* – large chastity-type elastic girdles with legs which reached the knees (mandatory, as I was to discover, for any respectable woman), they fanned themselves incessantly.

"*Dios mio*, such heat."

Their plump faces, innocent of make up, sweated profusely and dark rings of underarm sweat stained their straining blouses. Their hair, recently permed for the special occasion, hung sadly in damp frizzy curls.

Three nuns sat opposite, all wearing the same model of church-issue, owlish, wire-rimmed spectacles. The oldest of the three, Sister Dolores, had an impressive moustache and beady, censorious eyes. Her mouth wore a down-turned disapproving frown.

The two pretty younger nuns whispered between themselves and clasped their bibles and rosaries as if to ward off the evils that travelling by train might entail. They looked very hot in their habits, stockings and sensible shoes. I waited until Sister Dolores made her way to the toilet to attempt conversation.

"Hello, I'm Jill, what are your names? Are you going all the way to Málaga?"

They cast a nervous glance at the door in case the senior nun might return.

"I'm Clara and this is my cousin, Soledad," the younger nun almost whispered. "We've come from a convent in Madrid and we're going to Córdoba to join a convent there as novices. It's our first journey by train."

"But you are so young, why do you want to be nuns?" I asked curiously.

"Our families are not rich, and we have many brothers. There just isn't enough money to go round, and our brothers are the most important. My mother says it's a good opportunity for us girls and that we should be grateful. We will be Christ's brides."

"Does that mean you stay there for ever? What happens if you change your minds later and want to get married and have children?"

To my horror, tears began to roll down her cheeks. I hadn't meant to upset her. I must try to be more tactful. Perhaps my very basic knowledge of Spanish caused misunderstandings.

"I don't want to leave home, I don't want to be a nun," she cried, with deep heartrending sobs, "They'll cut off my hair. I want my mother."

"Don't cry, Clara," Soledad comforted the distraught girl, wiping a grubby handkerchief down her cheeks, "Father said that we could leave after six months if we're not happy."

"I'm so sorry, I spoke without thinking. They say Córdoba is beautiful and I am sure the nuns will be very kind to you. Don't cry, please."

It broke my heart to see such pretty young girls being carted off to spend their lives cooped up in a convent. But families were large and hunger rife. It was difficult to marry daughters off.

The carriage door slid open and Sister Dolores squeezed back into her seat.

"What's the matter? Why are you crying?"

"It's my fault, sister," I said. I hastened to repair the damage I had caused.

"I stupidly opened the window and some soot blew into Clara's eye. We were just trying to get it out."

She pursed her lips and clearly didn't believe me, but at that moment we stopped at a small station and a sweaty young man pushed his way into our compartment.

Miguel was in his thirties with thinning hair, a badly fitting shiny blue suit, and bad breath. He struggled onto the train with a large number of parcels and bags, which took up every available space.

"He's a *cosario*," explained Maria. "He's like a postman, carrying parcels from one town to the next by train. The roads are dangerous and so bad that the parcels would never get to the destinations otherwise. Don't you have them in your country?"

"No, I don't think we do, our roads are OK. We don't have bandits."

My spirits sank as I contemplated a lengthy journey under these cramped conditions. But as the arid, scorched countryside unfolded, the romance of the experience returned and reminded me why I was here, on this very slow train to Andalucía.

CHAPTER SEVEN

La Mancha

"Freedom is one of the most precious gifts that heaven gave man. Neither the treasures that the sea or the land contain can compare with freedom. One can and must risk one's life for freedom and honour, for captivity is the worst evil to befall mankind." – Don Quijote

Looking out of the grubby train window onto the sun-baked plains of the red earth of La Mancha, it was clear why the Moors named this part of Spain *"tierra seca"* – dry earth. The trees were systematically destroyed over the centuries by the Moors and the warring Christian armies, and only the occasional windmill broke the monotony. Here, Miguel de Cervantes wrote his major work, *Don Quijote de La Mancha*.

His creation, the whimsical Don Quijote, was convinced that he was a knight errant so he donned a suit of armour, and set out on his travels with his skinny horse, Rocinante, and his faithful squire and fat friend, Sancho Panza. Believing the windmills to be fierce giants he attacked them with his lance. Wayside inns became castles to be stormed and fat friars were kidnappers to be beaten. He attacked a herd of sheep with his lance, believing them to be an army, killing several in the process. Even a funeral party carrying the body of a nobleman did not escape his enthusiasm.

***

The heat was suffocating in our metal carriage and my clothes were drenched in sweat. The air outside was even hotter and any attempt to open the window drew growls of disapproval from my fellow travellers.

"Do you want to kill us all?" grumbled Miguel, coughing theatrically, "We'll breathe in the smoke from the engine."

I didn't care, and in my desperation to feel a slight breeze, managed to coax the window open a few inches.

As the train rounded a bend in the track, a blast of hot air and soot billowed from the funnel and we gasped as the fumes filled the carriage. I had not realised that the third class carriages were strategically placed just behind the engine, so that the more affluent passengers in second and first class did not have to suffer the smoke.

"I'm sorry, it's just so hot." I struggled to close the rusty catches, and subsided into my seat in embarrassment. Ana patted my arm kindly, and handed me her water container.

"Here, *niña*, you must drink or you'll be ill. You aren't accustomed to this heat."

I sipped the tepid water. Taking out Richard Ford's book, I turned to the chapter on the city of Córdoba, and, wiping away the sweat dripping into my eyes, I tried to concentrate on the city's chequered history.

Mile upon mile of dusty stubble fields and patchwork hills rolled by as the train rattled laboriously through the monotonous plains where even the windmills had mostly fallen into disuse. This inhospitable land was scorching in summer, but windblown and icy in winter. Gautier reported in winter a "furious wind sweeping the plain with the noise of thunder and an infinity of war chariots filled with armour".

At every stop, Miguel hurled a variety of parcels out of the window to be caught by his assistants who stood waiting on the platform, presumably to continue their journey to far-flung villages.

A sudden commotion in the now crowded corridor and the odour of cheap perfume had the ladies in our compartment bristling with outrage.

"What's happening Ana?" I stood up to get a better view.

"You'd best sit down child, it's not something a young girl needs to know about."

"Please tell me, or shall I go and look for myself?"

Sister Dolores was wobbling with anger.

"How dare they. It's a sin against the Church and the Virgin. It's shameful that these innocent young girls should see such behaviour."

I couldn't imagine what was happening and, with my usual curiosity, I climbed over Miguel's parcels, trampling the nuns' feet. It became clear that all the passengers from the next door compartment were now in the corridor. That is, all except one.

"What's happening? Is someone ill?"

"Ill, you could call it that." An infuriated matron shook her double chins. "That woman is a whore and she and a man in our compartment are..." she was suddenly at a loss for words.

A slightly calmer elderly lady whispered in my ear.

"My dear, they are doing what men and women do; it's how she makes money. She visits the carriages with male passengers looking for business. Unfortunately these 'ladies' carry all sorts of infections but the young men don't seem to care. Particularly the young soldiers on leave and the workers coming home on holiday from Germany and Italy. Of course we have to wait in the corridor until they have finished."

"But are they allowed to do this – what about the police?"

"Oh, they just turn a blind eye. I'm sure it's illegal, but it isn't called 'the world's oldest profession' for nothing. The *Guardia Civil* probably get paid to ignore what's going on."

Spain was definitely surprising. Bikinis were frowned upon but blatant prostitution was tolerated.

The compartment door opened and a heavily made up lady in her forties emerged, straightening her clothes. Chin in the air, she ignored the hail of insults from the indignant passengers as they returned to their seats, and spat theatrically out of the open window. The male culprit in the scenario seemed unmoved by the ill feeling and feigned sleep. Peace seemed to have been restored. That is, until she saw me.

She thrust her face into mine; her garlicky cigarette breath was nauseating. I took a hasty step backwards.

"What are you staring at Swedish girl?"

"I'm not Swedish, I'm English."

"It's all the same. You foreigners have ruined our business you know. Upsetting our men with your tight clothes and loose morals. And as for bikinis – they should be forbidden."

I gazed at her in astonishment.

"But I've only just arrived in Spain."

"Keep out of my way and off my patch. I've warned you. You'll regret it if I see you again."

"Well" said Ana, as I shakily resumed my seat "are you happy now? Did you see her?"

"Yes." I chose my words carefully. "The lady seemed very angry. It appeared that she thought I was going to take her clients away. What happens if the passengers refuse to move out of the compartment?"

"Oh, the couple just carry on, and usually everybody is so embarrassed they leave."

The monotony of the afternoon had certainly been relieved with this unexpected drama, and I resolved to keep well away from the lady in question.

***

Valdepeñas provided a welcome halt in my journey and the guard called out "*Treinta minutos*," – half an hour to stretch our legs, check out the station stalls and try a glass of the famous wine. Ana, Maria and I jumped down from the carriage, helped by a bronzed, good looking young soldier in the uniform of the Spanish foreign legion. His teeth were sparkling white as he laughed while his companions cheered at his gallantry. There was no time to leave the station but we pushed our way into the station taverna and ordered bread rolls stuffed with slices of tomato and olive oil.

"Will you try the wine, Maria?"

"We don't drink wine, *niña*. I'll just have a lemonade."

In the spirit of adventure, I decided to try out the famous red wine, but, after a few sips, agreed with Richard Ford, the famous

English author of *Gatherings From Spain*, that it would probably be better used in cooking. William Clark describes the wine as "execrable stuff" and remembered the inhabitants of Valdepeñas as being "ferocious and uncivil," whilst Gautier complains that the wine was "thick enough to cut with a knife and smelled horribly of pitch."

***

Back on board, we passed large flocks of sheep searching for the meagre pickings in the stubble fields. They are bred for their milk and the famous *manchego* cheese, and were herded by small boys with slings, dressed in sheepskin jerkins, who waved and shouted at the train as we passed. The flocks are guarded by powerful Spanish mastiff dogs, equipped with large collars and leather chest protectors with metal spikes to deter the wolves.

A few abandoned farmhouses bore witness to the mass emigration of the peasant farmers to the cities and to the factories of Germany and Belgium. Lack of food and work after the Spanish Civil War forced these farmworkers to leave their homes and families to seek underpaid and monotonous work in ghettos with little prospect of integration or improving their conditions.

Once a year, the great migration home occurred in the first week of August. Then, during the last weekend, the roads and trains were once again crammed with workers returning to their dreary existence for another year.

At the narrow mountain pass of Despeñaperros, La Mancha ends and the region of Andalucía begins. The pass was the only route from the north to the south of the country and, until the construction of the railway, the bandits and smugglers found rich pickings from the continual horse-drawn traffic. The roads and ravines were narrow and potholed, making progress slow for carriages and mule trains, so it was easy for the *bandoleros* to stop unprotected travellers. The early nineteenth-century 'gentleman bandit', José Maria el Tempranillo, was one of Spain's most famous highwaymen. He operated on this road for some years with impunity. This became such a problem in the that it was decided to colonize Despeñaperros to displace the bandits. The Spanish government offered peasants from Germany and Holland a house, a yoke of oxen, and food for one year if they would live in this area and farm the land. The offer specifically banned all hairdressers or actors, since their skills were deemed superfluous in the eradication of banditry, although all other professions were welcomed. Irish traveller Sir John Talbot Dillon wrote of the toll to cross the pass that had to be paid by all travellers with 'monkeys, parrots or negroes'. Married women were exempt if travelling in the company of their husbands or upon producing a certificate of marriage. The train rumbled through the rocky gorges of the Sierra Morena, the brown mountains made famous by Don Quijote. The tunnels were dark and threatening and offered a reprieve from the sun, but not from the heat. It was a relief to burst out into the sunlight the far end.

"You know there are bears here as well as wolves," Maria shuddered. "Imagine coming face to face with one."

I peered out hopefully but the grime on the windows of the carriage made it impossible to see much, let alone a timid bear in broad daylight.

"This journey seems endless. How much longer till we get to Córdoba, Maria?"

"At least not till tomorrow morning – early, about 7 I think."

As the train made its way out of the ravine, the arid plains of La Mancha gradually gave way to gentle hillsides of Andalucía with olive trees laid out in serried ranks, mile upon mile of grey earth and endless straight lines of trees laden with maturing fruit. Fields of golden sunflowers revolved their faces to catch the last of the sun's rays; hillsides were carpeted with scarlet poppies mingling with the ripening wheat.

"I plan to stop in Córdoba for a night. It's probably the only chance I have to see the city." I told Ana.

She immediately invited me to stay with her family.

"My home is your home."

"I couldn't accept, you hardly know me".

"Nonsense, you will be much safer with my family. It's not right for a young girl like you to be alone in a city you don't know."

Finally, I allowed myself to be persuaded. I could catch the mail train to Málaga early next morning and it would be a welcome respite from the gruelling heat of the tin carriage.

At least Ana and Maria hadn't poured such scorn on my proposed journey across the mountains as had my earlier travelling companions.

"Where will you sleep on your journey?" asked Ana. "Are there hostels in the mountains?"

"I am told we will sleep in *posadas*, muleteers' inns, with the horses," I told her.

"*Que horror*. There will be flies, and probably fleas."

Ana was horrified; Maria was more concerned about the food.

"In those mountain villages goodness knows what there will be to eat" she worried. "Probably there isn't even any electricity."

Ana brushed aside Maria's misgivings about the probable culinary deficiencies in the mountains.

"More important, what about these bandits you talked about. What if they really still exist? You may be robbed, or even killed."

Laughing, I teased, "Sadly, Ana, I think they are all dead, but I hope to find a good-looking one. Imagine riding away into his mountain hideout on a big black stallion and falling in love and living happily ever after"

She gave me a reproving look and pursed her lips.

"No, really Ana, I will be careful, and I am sure we will be safe. I don't have too much that a bandit would want to steal."

Slightly mollified, she closed her fan with a loud click. Folding her arms across her ample bosom she was determined to have the last word.

"I'm sure your mother wouldn't approve," she said accusingly, and closed her eyes to signify an end to the conversation.

***

Darkness fell and the heat slowly abated. The squashed and oily remains of the tortilla were produced and shared out by Maria; the three nuns contenting themselves with rolls filled with spicy sausage, purchased at the last station. Miguel, the travelling postman, fished a tin of tuna fish out of his bag and a loaf of bread, and ate noisily off the blade of his a pocket knife. Exhausted from the unrelenting heat, we all dozed fitfully on the unforgiving wooden seats. Miguel's mouth fell open as he snored loudly, and Sister Dolores clicked her rosary endlessly as she murmured prayers to an unseen god.

The train trundled noisily through the night, seemingly stopping at every village in Andalucía. No-one entered our compartment, due to the pile of parcels with which Miguel had filled every available space. The closer we came to Córdoba, the more animated Ana and Maria became, as they told me of their families who were waiting for them and how much they would have to tell them.

"My boys," Maria proudly pulled a dog-eared photograph of her sons – two small boys smiling self-consciously, dressed in sailor suits, on their First Communion day – from her purse. It was the first time the two women had been so far from home, on a visit to Ana's cousin, Amelia, who lived in Madrid with a foreigner called Peter.

"He's a good man, and he works hard," she confided. "He's a little strange, but then he's foreign. And he's good to my cousin Amelia."

"They met during the troubles you know, the war," she whispered, glancing at the nuns to see if they were listening. Reassured, she moved to sit closer to me.

"It was terrible in Madrid," she said as she clicked her fan nervously, "bodies in the streets, and so many young men killed. I was in Córdoba but Amelia and her family were in the city. They were reported as being communists, Reds, and were all arrested. Amelia was only eighteen. They never knew who reported them, and they were no more communists than I am. She never saw her parents again." She shuddered and wiped away a tear. "Amelia was raped by the soldiers and gave birth to a baby girl. It was terrifying for her, so young and all alone."

"What happened to the baby?"

"You'd never believe it, but those wicked nuns in the hospital told her it was going to be taken away to be educated by a good patriotic family. They called her a Red communist whore. That's religion for you."

"How ghastly. Did she ever know what happened to her daughter?"

"No, she was all alone in the world. They shaved her head and painted it red before they released her. She had no money and no way of caring for a child even if she could have found out where she had been taken. I couldn't help her either. That was when she met Peter. He was wounded during a battle outside the city and my cousin hid him in a cellar for months until he was well."

From what I had read about the civil war, I assumed that he was probably one of the International Brigade volunteers, who joined the republican ranks against General Franco's army. But Maria was frowning and Ana, shaking her head and with a finger to her lips, was warning me against asking more questions. I realised that further indiscreet conversation could place her whole family in danger, but Miguel continued to snore and Sister Dolores gave no signs of interrupting her prayers. What sort of religion encouraged the kidnapping of babies?

CHAPTER EIGHT

Córdoba

*"Córdoba is now a melancholy place, a sad example of
a nation's decline; mournful evidence of what mighty
Spain once was – a deathlike stillness and the decay of
ancient grandeur."* – A.C. Andros

We arrived in Córdoba as dawn broke. The relief of arriving and
taking a break from the hot and steamy train was tremendous.

"Look at the *mezquita*," said Ana as she pointed excitedly at the
silhouette of the mosque against the dark blue sky. Such a famous
city, so many ghosts.

Baron D'Avillier praised the mosque above even the renowned
Alhambra in Granada. As early as the seventh century, street
lighting was installed in the city, when London and Paris were
still in the dark ages. The photographs in my guide book showed
majestic Moorish architecture yet when George Borrow visited he
found it "poor, dirty and sad", Richard Ford described "an oriental
aspect but above all, decadence" and Louisa Tenison, an intrepid
female traveller, commented a hundred years earlier, that Córdoba
is deserted and abandoned. The whistle of the steam engine will yet
rouse the slumbering valleys and the smoke of the locomotive curl
in wreathed clouds over the plain.

Since the departure of the Moors and the Jews, in the late fifteenth
and early sixteenth century, it appeared that the beautiful city and

its culture had been sadly neglected, but the majesty of the great mosque was surely untouchable and I wanted to explore. I was also keen to see the Jewish quarter, which had been the scene of so much violence when the Jews were expelled.

I wasn't sure of the correct way to say goodbye to the three nuns, so took my lead from Maria who kissed each of them on both cheeks and wished them God speed.

"Have a good journey, sisters."

Clara looked pale and tears welled in her eyes again. I gave her an extra hug.

"It'll be fine – you'll see."

Miguel, the taciturn *cosario*, was also leaving the train, and there was much pushing and shoving as we all attempted to unload packages and suitcases through the narrow doors. Both Ana's brother and Maria's husband were there to help.

"Come on, Jill."

I hung back, somewhat embarrassed by the endless round of kissing and hugging, not sure if Ana's family would be too keen to have an unknown foreign girl staying with them. But they hustled me along and we piled into an ancient taxi and bumped over the cobbled streets to the pretty little apartment in the old part of the town, where Ana lived with her widowed mother and her brother. It was still early and the town was quiet, with the odd donkey trudging the streets on its bread round and long lines of mules bringing fruit and vegetables to the market. Even at that early hour the air was heavy and a slight haze promised another scorching day.

Ana's mother, Lola, was a stout middle-aged lady, who had dressed in black since the death of her husband. She greeted me like a long-lost daughter, horrified to hear that I was travelling alone,

"*Que miedo,*" – *how scary* – she kept repeating to herself, and busied herself with big cups of hot chocolate and toast.

"Eat, you must eat. I suffer from my nerves, you know, ever since the death of my dear husband, and then my sister, and her husband in Madrid. We live in difficult times. God rest their souls in peace."

She crossed herself and wiped way a tear. Laying a hand on her breast as if to calm her nerves she seemed to drift into a world of memories. But her spirits were soon restored and she and Ana chattered away like two starlings, reliving the excitement of Ana's trip. Ana's brother, Julio, didn't get a chance to speak, and just sat quietly, smiling apologetically at me now and then.

But I had no time to waste, and I wanted to see the city. I asked Ana if I might leave to visit the mosque. Lola wrung her hands with concern at the dangers faced by a young girl alone with so many bad people loose on the streets, until she hit on a happy solution.

How stupid, she said, why hadn't she thought of it before? Her sister Concepcion's son, who went by the name of Aníbal, was training to be a tourist guide and would surely like to practise his English. It would be much more proper for me to be escorted and he was very dependable. She clapped her hands with pleasure at such an excellent solution to the problem and immediately dispatched Julio to summon my escort.

Aníbal, a tall, dark young man of about 25, arrived looking distinctly unenthusiastic at his aunt's orders to escort me. As moral support he had brought his friend Jesús, who spoke no English at all but was an attractive young man with spiky black hair, big brown eyes and luxuriant long eyelashes that most girls would die for. His smooth brown skin bore witness to his Moorish ancestry. Aníbal, on the other hand, had drawn the short straw in the personality stakes and his thick glasses and flat feet didn't immediately bring to mind his conquering Carthaginian namesake. But we were stuck with each other for the day, so I smiled at him encouragingly and threw out a few tentative Spanish phrases about how excited I was to be in Córdoba. He sighed and blinked nervously,

"OK, we go," he announced resignedly.

Escorted by my two minders, and clutching Richard Ford's book in case Hannibal's tourist guide training had not advanced past stage one, we sallied forth to the sights. I had found plenty of time on the train to read up on the history so that all Aníbal would need to do was to steer us in the right direction.

It seems that the Carthaginians named the city Karduba, the City of Juba, in honour of General Juba who died in battle here in 230 BC. The Romans changed the name to Corduba in 206 BC, and the region became known for its olive oil production. Both Julius Caesar and Hannibal spent time here (hence my guide's name). Situated on the Rio Guadalquivir, meaning the "Great River" in Arabic, its position was of supreme importance to all invading armies. On the river bank was the giant Roman waterwheel that supplied the city in time of siege.

Many races have had a foothold in Spain, amongst them the Iberians, Celts, Phoenicians, Romans, Carthaginians, Goths, Vandals, and Moors. But none of these invaders have managed to fuse the Spanish races into a concrete whole. However powerful they were in Al Andalus, even the Moors failed to unite the rest of Spain, which was ultimately their undoing

Indeed, the Romans were so hated that entire villages committed mass suicide rather than be taken by the invader. In the Peninsular War, Wellington and Napoleon battled it out, after the French had invaded Spain.

I soon realised that I had underestimated young Aníbal and he and Jesús made good guides, clearly warming to my evident fascination with their city. They told me that the word "Moor" was initially used to refer to Islamic invaders from Morocco, usually Arabs or Turks, and the word *Moro* is still used today as a derogatory term for anyone of African descent, mainly north Africans.

The *Moros* arrived in Spain in the 711 when Tariq ibn Ziyad, their commander, crossed the straits of Gibraltar with twelve thousand men. His soldiers were not Arab but Berbers from the Rif mountains, and it was not until some years later that the Arabs themselves arrived in Spain. Tariq overthrew the hastily collected forces of King Roderic and swept across the country.

"Before us is the enemy, behind us the sea," Tariq said on landing in Spain. "We have only one chance – to win."

As their armies moved north they defeated the Christians and decimated the existing population. The Christians and the Mohammedans were almost incessantly at war with each other, and it took the Christians more than seven hundred years to reclaim their soil.

For many years the Jews lived in relative harmony with the Christians and the Moors, acting as mediators in the frequent squabbles between these two main powers. Battles waged continuously as the Christians attempted to recover Spain, but Islamic power lasted under some guise or other until the end of the fifteenth century. Christians and Jews were allowed to practise their religions but were more heavily taxed. Towns were taken and lost again. The Roman irrigation system was repaired, and agriculture flourished. Spain was celebrated in the known world for the civilization established under Moorish domination. George Dennis wrote that Andalucía was the "territory earliest seized, most fondly cherished and longest held by the chivalrous and polished Arabs".

Both Jesús and Aníbal were a little sketchy on dates, but, assisted by my guide book, we muddled through and grasped the main flow of the Moorish dynasties. In his rather disjointed English, Aníbal told me about the Emir Abdul Rahman I who had been forced to leave Damascus in 756 when his family was massacred. He founded the first autonomous emirate in Al Andalus in Córdoba, where he established free schools that both girls and boys attended. Wise men were invited to found centres of learning and it became known as the Athens of the west. Razis, a famous physician of the time, called Córdoba "the nurse of sciences, the cradle of warriors," and he wrote a thesis on anaesthetics. In an era when the population of northern Europe was mostly illiterate, even women played an important part in the professions of the Moorish cities, as teachers, doctors, and lawyers. Seneca was born here. Jewish scholars from Córdoba, taught by the Moors, set up the equivalent of the University of Oxford, and the library contained 400,000 books

The emir ordered a palm tree to be planted beside the mosque to remind him of his home land. It is said that all palms in Spain descend from this tree. Homesick for his country, he wrote:

> Beautiful palm tree,
> Like me thou art a stranger in the land.

His household numbered over six thousand, made up of wives,

concubines, and black eunuchs. It was said that on the battlefield he was accompanied by twelve thousand horsemen whose belts and scimitars were studded with gold.

We strolled through the cobbled streets, marvelling at the size and grandeur of the mosque, which Aníbal told me had been built on the site of a Christian church. The emir had kept his promise to build a mosque that would be greater than that of his beloved home town of Damascus. He drew up the plans himself and worked on the building each day with his own hands. In his haste to complete the task he ordered marble columns to be brought from cities in Africa, Spain, and France. It is said that the earth was transported from Narbonne in France by Christian prisoners who carried it on their backs. However, the emir died before he could finish the mosque and it was left to his son to complete the work, in the latter half of the tenth century. When the Christians took Córdoba in 1236, construction of a cathedral within the mosque was commenced. The result is a cocktail of architecture: Gothic, Moorish, renaissance and baroque.

As we approached the mosque, we passed through the *Patio de Los Naranjos*, a pretty square planted with orange trees and with irrigation channels let into the mud tiles to cool the air. An Arab historian relates that when the Caliph Al-Mansur wished to build the patio, he expropriated several houses that stood in his way. He offered the owners a fair price and another house. Only one old woman refused to sell. There was a palm tree in her courtyard and she refused to move unless she was given a house with a similar tree. The Caliph gave the order to comply with her wishes and, at great expense, another house, complete with palm tree, was purchased for her.

As we passed, the human flotsam resulting from the ferocity of the civil war milled around the orange-fragrant patio, in search of a peseta or two or the remains of a tourist's sandwich. The legless and the blind pulled at passing trouser legs and held up misspelt messages asking for alms. Several sad, wrinkled old ladies swathed in black sat on the ground outside the mosque with begging bowls in their lap.

"Why are all these people hungry Aníbal? Is there no-one who looks after them?"

"They were probably on the wrong side in the war," he spoke quietly. "If they were on the republican side nobody will dare help them."

"But the war was over twenty years ago," I whispered.

"We must not talk about it," he said firmly. "It is not allowed and will only make trouble. We have a great leader now, General Franco, and we have order and peace. The republicans were communists and killed many people."

I was uncertain whether this was what he believed, but it was clearly the official line. After all, he was only a baby when the war ended. Jesús had moved away from us, as if to disassociate himself from this dangerous line of conversation, and was shuffling his feet nervously.

I evidently had a lot to learn, and was upsetting my young guides with my questions. My curiosity was again getting me into trouble. I didn't pursue the question, and changed the subject.

"Let's go into the mosque, out of the sun. I really want to see the painted ceilings."

Jostling with groups of tourists loaded with cameras and guide books, we entered the historic building. We strolled through the majestic columns and the wide marble walkways, pausing to admire the minaret and the elaborate Moorish mosaics.

The mosque was lit by thousands of lamps. Caliph Al-Mansur had commanded that the bells from the cathedral in Santiago de Compostela be brought to Córdoba by Christian slaves. They were upended and suspended from the roof on silver chains to serve as additional lighting. After the Christian King Fernando III (known as *el Santo*, the The Saint) took Córdoba in 1236 it was the turn of the Moorish slaves to carry the bells to be placed in another Cathedral, this time in Santiago de Compostela.

CHAPTER NINE

The Inquisition and the Christian Monarchs

"So far can fanaticism pervert the minds of even the purest to sanction the vilest cruelties, under the mistaken idea of furthering a religion, which preached peace on earth and goodwill towards men."
– Louisa Tenison

My feet were aching and my brain was struggling with so much history and legends of emirs, caliphs and kings.

"I'm gasping for a drink, can we stop somewhere? Drinks are on me."

Aníbal considered this. "Women aren't really allowed in bars, but we can go to one owned by my family. I don't think that would matter."

So we repaired to a tiny bar in one of the narrow side-streets in search of a cold drink and a plate of the local delicacy: deep fried aubergines covered in sticky cane honey. The young men appeared to have recovered from their discomfiture and fear caused by my questions about the Spanish Civil War. I realised that I needed to be more tactful, and that there was a real danger for them if they didn't toe the official line and condemn the republican losers in the conflict.

The owner of the bar was pleased to see the two boys.

"Paco is my cousin," Aníbal explained, "and Dolores, his wife, is a wonderful cook."

On hearing their voices a large twinkly lady stuck her head through the plastic fly curtain covering the entrance to the kitchen. Wiping her hands on her apron, she leaned over the bar and kissed the boys on each cheek.

"*Hola, chicos*. What brings you boys here with this pretty *señorita*?"

Aníbal explained that his aunt had foisted me on them for the day.

"Make them work hard," she winked at me. "Boys of today don't know what work is."

"Don't nag, woman," Paco reprimanded his wife, "get back in the kitchen and prepare these boys something to eat. What can I get you *señorita*?"

We ordered a glass of ice-cold *fino* wine from Montilla for me and lemonade for the two boys.

When we had quenched our thirst and done justice to a large plate of fried squid to accompany the sticky aubergines, I quizzed Aníbal on a safer political subject.

I was fascinated by all I had read about the part that the energetic young Christian monarchs had played in the history of Spain. Their daughter, Catherine, became the wife of English Henry VIII.

"Aníbal, please tell me about King Fernando and Queen Isabella. They seem to have been very powerful."

He heaved a sigh of relief at this non-contentious subject, polished his glasses and settled back into his chair. He seemed well versed in the story of the crusading royal pair. Prompted by Jesús, he told me their story.

"Fernando, King of Aragon, was only seventeen when he married Isabella, Queen of Castile, in 1469. Isabella's family would have preferred her to marry Alfonso V, King of Portugal, thus unifying the two countries, but Fernando was young and good looking, while Alfonso was old and ugly. She had already rejected Louis XI of France, and the future Richard III of England.

Fernando was tall, dark and attractive "with a pleasant face and laughing eyes". There was no contest in Isabella's mind; she would marry him, and, even at her young age, she was clearly a force to be reckoned with. She was not concerned at his reputation as a precocious womaniser – indeed he already had two illegitimate children by the time he was seventeen. But after their marriage she was reported to be prone to fits of jealousy and made sure that her ladies-in-waiting had no opportunity to dally with her attractive and powerful husband. Since the young pair were cousins, they needed the Pope's express permission to marry, and the current pope refused to grant their request. Their creative solution was to forge a pre-dated letter of permission from the previous Pope who had died five years earlier. Their marriage unified Spain (except for Navarra and Granada, both of which remained under Moorish rule), and changed the face of Spanish history.

The young monarchs were also the brains behind the infamous Spanish Inquisition, which did incalculable harm to literature, art, and the prosperity of Spain. Isabella was a religious fanatic and determined to stamp out heresy. Fernando acted from political ambition and he coveted the riches and lands belonging to these 'heretics'.

By 1486, most of the Jews living in Aragon had already been expelled. However, the support and financial donations of the Jews in Andalucía, and Granada in particular, were needed in the campaign against the Moors. There was, therefore, a stay of execution for these Jews until their funds became redundant. Tomás de Torquemada, in charge of the Inquisition, agreed to wait until Granada fell, which it did in 1492."

"Yes," I interrupted. "I have seen a painting which shows the moment when Fernando announced that he had decided not to expel the Granada Jews in exchange for a loan of thirty thousand ducats. He badly needed the funds to pay his armies."

"Yes, but this got him in trouble with Torquemada who was furious," Aníbal continued.

"He burst into the chamber where the Jews' leaders and the monarchs were in conference, brandishing a crucifix and shouting: 'Judas Iscariot betrayed our Lord for thirty pieces of silver. The kings of Spain would sell him a second time for thirty thousand'. Hurling the crucifix onto the table before the astonished monarchs, he cried,

'Take him and barter him for thirty pieces of silver.' The last Jews were expelled, and Torquemada had his way."

"So, what happened to the Jews?"

"Well, Isabella and Fernando had already persuaded the Pope to authorize a special branch of the Spanish Inquisition to search out heretics, purify the Christian church, and restore order. They soon announced their decision "to banish all Jews of both sexes for ever from the precincts of our realm".

"The Inquisition now had the green light to 'investigate' the wealthy Jews in Granada, who were given the choice of leaving Spain with all their belongings except gold, coins, jewels or silver; or converting to Christianity. The chief rabbi visited Isabella to beg her to annul the expulsion decree, believing her to be the chief instigator. She replied:

"Did you think this came from me? You are wrong, God put this thought into the King's heart."

Almost certainly she lied about her influence over the king. Between them Torquemada and Isabella persuaded the indecisive King that the confiscation of the Jews' properties would solve his financial problems. As a result he took the decision to sign the infamous Alhambra Decree of expulsion and the blood of many thousands of Jews was on their hands. The Jews called Fernando the incarnation of evil, and his wife Jezebel.

"About fifty thousand Jews and Moors chose to convert to Christianity. Christianized Jews were known as the *conversos*, whilst Christianized Moors were known as *moriscos*. Many of these Jewish families, who had been pressurized into converting, secretly practised their faith behind locked doors. They were mercilessly and fanatically hunted down by the Inquisitors. Attempts were made to determine whether a person had Jewish blood among his ancestors. After so many centuries of Jewish presence in Spain it was almost certain that every family would be found guilty of this 'crime'. The graveyards were ransacked by the Inquisitors and, if a deceased were reported to have had Jewish leanings during his life his bones were exhumed and burned. His descendants could no longer hold public office. The Pope, horrified at the result of his permission for the Inquisition, revoked his authorization and demanded that the persecution stop.

The *moriscos* were also treated with studied cruelty. They were forbidden to use their language or customary dress. The women had to be unveiled and their houses open to public view. A rumour was circulated that their children were to be taken away and sent to live in Castile. They were prohibited to bathe or celebrate weddings, and all Moorish music was banned. In effect, the Moorish culture that had lasted eleven centuries in Spain was outlawed. In 1502 forcible conversion began again and in 1568 a revolt in Granada commenced a savage civil war."

"Yes," I interrupted, "I read D'Avillier's account of some of the revolting atrocities that were committed on both sides. It was such unbelievable cruelty."

"Villages were razed to the ground and thousands burned at the stake. In one town, the Moors boiled the monks of the convent in oil; in another, once the Spanish garrison had left, they stuffed the priest full of gunpowder and fired him like a rocket. The Moors sacrificed children on a butcher's stall, and devoured the heart of a Christian they had murdered. A village priest was torn limb from limb by the villagers. It seems that a barbaric blood lust had overtaken them all.

In the siege of the castle at Jubilez, a thousand Moorish women were beheaded after desperately attempting to blind the invading Christian troops by throwing sand in their eyes. Moorish fathers buried their daughters alive in the snow, rather than have them fall into the hands of their enemies. Inevitably the *moriscos* lost, and most of the survivors – converted and unconverted – were sent to the north of Spain. Three hundred thousand were sent in galleys to Africa. In each village, two families were left to care for the silk worms and look after the running and maintenance of the irrigation systems."

"But I thought that the Inquisition was mainly in Seville."

"Yes," agreed Aníbal, "and in the first year 298 victims were burned at the stake in the city. Tomás de Torquemada was in charge and in his sixteen years in the post, nine thousand people were condemned to death. He himself came from a family of *conversos*, which perhaps made him more diligent. No-one was safe from the reign of terror and the intolerance of the notorious and zealous

Inquisitor-in-Chief. The examinations and trials would last months; victims were most horribly tortured.

I shuddered. "I can't imagine how people lived under this type of terror. So many of them had done nothing wrong. They were just ignorant."

I had also read excerpts from Dr Wylie's *History of Protestantism* where he describes some of the common forms of torture:

> There were instruments for compressing fingers until the bones splintered – instruments for probing under the finger nails or tearing out the tongue – cradles full of sharp spikes – iron ladles for pouring molten lead or boiling pitch down the throats of the victims – ingenious instruments for pinching, probing or tearing sensitive parts of the body and continuing the pain up to the very verge where reason or life gives way.

Not only did the prisoners have to repent and confess, but to be spared with only a penance they needed to denounce "any accomplice who shared the error". After being declared guilty a prisoner's property was confiscated and an *auto da fe* – an act of faith – took place. The aristocracy, black-clad local dignitaries, and gawking townspeople attended these events as did robed priests who escorted the prisoners from the dungeons. The prisoners were clothed in a woollen smock with a yellow and scarlet cross on the chest, decorated with devils and flames. A paper mitre was placed on their heads, a rope of broom twisted around their necks and a green wax taper put in their hands. Their sentences were read out and they were invited to repent in a public act of penance. Crowds flocked to see those condemned to die marching slowly to their place of doom. They were then taken away to be burned at the stake in a separate, secular ceremony since the Catholic Church could not be seen to shed blood. Regardless of whether they were condemned to death or merely life imprisonment, all were relieved of their property.

The Inquisition expelled Jews, Moors, Christian heretics, and many thousands of Spain's wealthiest citizens and intellectuals.

Once again it seemed that religion and bigotry was an excuse for appalling atrocities. So much tragic suffering – I felt quite despondent, and my young guides, fearing that they had strayed into dark territory, decided that no more should be said about torture and execution.

CHAPTER TEN

The Diaspora of the Jews

*"Weep, weep you women for well may you weep for the
Holy City and the destruction of Zion."*
– Jewish funeral lyric

"So, where do you come from? Why are you in Spain?" asked
Jesús.

I enthusiastically told him of my proposed journey retracing the
steps of the early travellers, riding through the mountains, looking
out for bandits, and so on. But neither boy had heard of Richard
Ford or D'Avillier and Aníbal obviously agreed with his aunt Ana
that I was quite mad to go riding around on dangerous horses in the
August heat.

"Why do that?" he chewed on a toothpick, "It'll be horribly hot
and you'll be eaten by mosquitoes."

It was obvious that he was not a romantic, but quite content with
what was, in my opinion, an unexciting existence.

"I go to the university here in Córdoba, but I have failed my
exams this year," he told me.

Jesús had more ambition and wanted to go to England to further
his English studies.

"I really need to get a job in London – do you think you can
help?"

"You might get a job in a pub or something, but you need to work
harder at learning English. I'll see what I can do when I get home."

"Shall we go? There is still lots to see."

Aníbal was keen to continue the tourist route he was familiar with, but after all I had heard about their suffering, I wanted to see the Jewish quarter, or *kahal*.

We enjoyed the respite from the sun as we walked through the maze of narrow streets towards the synagogue in the Street of the Jews. The houses were so close together that neighbours' upstairs windows almost met in some places. I closed my eyes and imagined the terror of the many attacks on the defenceless families. The Spanish Jews called Spain "*Sepharad*", and considered it the second Jerusalem. But they were caught between Islam and Christianity, never quite accepted despite the important part they played in society. They were feared and hated for their wealth, for being money lenders and for being the king's official tax collectors. Further north in Burgos, an inflamed mob with torches and swords attacked the sleeping Jews and slaughtered men, women and children, throwing them from windows or burning them to death in their houses. Only those who threw themselves on their knees, begging to be accepted into the Christian church were spared.

Footsteps sounded behind us, soft on the cobbled street, bringing me back from my thoughts.

"Where are you off to, Aníbal?"

"Oh, hi Aarón, we're showing the *kahal* to this friend of my aunt's."

The two boys embraced.

"You've really picked the hottest part of the day. Do you want to come to my house for a cold drink?"

"What do you think, Jill?"

"Yes, I'd love to see his house. But I don't want to intrude."

"No problem, my parents will be pleased to welcome you.," said Aarón formally.

We continued through the maze of narrow cobbled streets, each house seemingly identical to its neighbour. Through ornate iron doors we caught a glimpse of patios adorned with pots of geraniums and carnations of every colour. Many doors and windows were boarded up and plants grew out of neglected cracks in the walls. The *kahal* was as it had been for centuries, untouched by modern daily life. Only chattering groups of sweating tourists, led by guides waving flags, infested the wider streets and the tourist route to the synagogue.

Aarón stopped at last in front of a small wooden door.

"Welcome to my home."

We squeezed into the small sitting room, dark and cool.

"Is that you Aarón?"

"Yes, I've brought Aníbal and some friends."

A slim, olive-skinned lady of about 40 came through from the kitchen, drying her hands. A broad smile lit up her face at the sight of so many young people crowding into her house.

"Welcome. Aníbal. It's a delight to see you again."

"They've come for a cold drink, mother. Jill is visiting Córdoba."

"You've found yourself a good guide. Come sit with me, Jill, I'm Judith. My husband Samuel will be back soon when he closes the shop."

The small house smelled musty, but I also caught the faint fragrance of oranges.

"I don't want to intrude, but I'm fascinated by the history of the *kahal*. Has your family always lived here?"

"Yes, four generations of us. Our grandparents, and theirs before them, have always had jewellery shops here. Most of our neighbours have been here for a long time also. But as you can see, a lot of the houses are empty. Times have been difficult."

"I've read about a lot of trouble when the houses were burned and Jews had to convert or be killed."

Judith sipped her drink thoughtfully.

"That was many hundreds of years ago, but you're right. There are few of us left here now. But at least we are left in peace to follow our beliefs."

The boys had tired of the conversation and were lounging in the street, gawping at the girls leaving the school close by.

Samuel arrived and kissed his wife

"This is Jill. She's visiting the city. We're just talking about the history of the *kahal*. You're the expert here. I'll leave you to tell her. I'll just get us something to eat."

"Please don't bother yourself, Judith. We just ate at Paco's bar".

"I'm sure you will have room for some of my apple cakes," she said as she bustled from the room.

Samuel was many years older than his wife – grey haired with dark shadows under his eyes. His suit was worn and his shoes scuffed. His spectacles gave him a bird-like air and life did not appear to have treated him well. He took the old rocking chair with the embroidered cushion.

"Bring me a cold drink, wife. I'm parched. So, *señorita*, what do you want to know about our Jewish history?"

"I can't believe I'm finally here in the Jewish quarter.

I've read so much about the diaspora of the Jews from Córdoba and the terrible death of those children. It's said that King Manuel's evil solution to the elimination of further generations of Jews was to send all their children away to die."

"The murder of all those Jewish children in Portugal was all the fault of that wicked Queen Isabella," said Samuel. "Not content with expelling all the Jews from Spain, she also had to make the King of Portugal expel them too. So not only did the Jews have to pay a tax to cross the border into Portugal, but then the king sent all their children to be eaten by lizards on that terrible Sao Tome Island. He was between the devil and the deep blue sea – he wanted the wealth the Jews brought him, but he also wanted to marry Queen Isabella's beautiful daughter. So he had to get rid of the Jews.

"Did you know that more that more than 300,000 Jews were expelled from Andalucía? They left behind their homes and valuables and travelled only with their clothes and any items of value they could hide. During their last days in Spain, they spent many hours in the Jewish cemeteries, praying at the graves of their ancestors.

"Some of our most famous Jewish historians tell the story of the departure of our people." Samuel picked up a book lying on the table beside him, and opened it a well marked page. "Listen to what this says. 'Most were on foot. Some were lucky and rode on a mule or a horse, loaded with their belongings. Many collapsed from exhaustion, some fell ill, some died, some were born alongside the dead. The Christians ran among them and begged the Jews to accept conversion and save themselves, but the rabbis intervened and encouraged the Jews to stand firm in their faith, whatever the consequences. When they arrived at the beach they were placed in boats; many, dangerously overloaded, sank close to the shore.'"

A tear ran down Samuel's cheek.

"Just imagine the scene on those beaches. Many were taken by pirates. The men were to be sold as slaves, but the pirates kept the women, to rape them and then to search them for any gold or jewels they might have concealed. Some had hidden gold coins in their hair or their shoes, but those who had nothing of interest were searched more thoroughly. The women's throats were cut; their stomachs and intestines sliced as the pirates searched for hidden coins. With each new find of gold or jewels the zeal of the pirate band would be renewed, as the pile of riches grew alongside the pile of mutilated bodies. Many of the Jewish women raped by Muslims were killed to prevent them giving birth to a child who would be raised as a Jew – an anathema to a Muslim. Thousands of Jews died of hunger and thirst in the boats or were shipwrecked on small islands with no food or water. On arrival at foreign ports they were refused entry. At least the Turkish Jews allowed the refugees to land and the Chief Rabbi of Constantinople paid the ransom to rescue many from the hands of the pirates."

By now Samuel was weeping openly. Judith put her arm round his shoulders.

"Don't upset yourself, husband. That was very many years ago. We are safe in Spain and so are our children." Judith wiped his tears. "Here, Jill, try some of my cakes, they are made of apple and cinnamon to my grandmother's recipe."

Once again I had caused distress.

"Samuel, I'm so sorry I have upset you. I just wanted to understand some of your fascinating history. Is it true that many Sephardic Jews still keep the keys of their Andalucían houses?"

"It seems unbelievable. But they have Spain in their blood."

"Those cakes are delicious, Judith. I love cinnamon. And what lovely candlesticks. They look really old."

Judith beamed.

"They're silver and have been handed down through generations. Heaven knows how old they are. Look, they have eight branches, we light them at the Chanukah festival."

Aníbal was hovering anxiously in the doorway.

"We really should go."

"Yes, you're right, we should leave Judith and Samuel in peace."

As we left I noticed a small box fixed on the door post.

"What's that for, Judith?"

She ran her hand over the elaborately carved wooden box. "It contains a mezuzah a piece of parchment with verses from our Torah, reminding us to live as God wants us to. A home with a mezuzah is believed to be protected by God, and some devout Jewish families have one on each doorway in their homes."

"Don't worry about Samuel," Judith reassured me as she kissed me goodbye. "He's getting old. He gets very worked up at old memories, but it soon passes."

I bid farewell to the family, thanking them for their hospitality.

The boys were keen to finish their day's work and deliver me back to Ana. I, too, was tired and we made our way back to the apartment. Jesús bade me farewell in the street. I promised to write via Ana if I could find him a job in London. Ana opened the door.

"How did it go?"

"Really fantastic," I told her. "Aníbal is so knowledgeable about the city."

"But of course," Ana smiled proudly.

"I'm so grateful to him. But he must be tired, please let him go home."

Aníbal couldn't wait to give his aunt a perfunctory kiss, and disappeared down the stairs before she could find another job for him.

Freshly showered and in clean clothes, I sat on their little terrace sipping home-made lemonade and reflecting on just how lucky I had been. The boys had been great young guides, and the Jewish family were incredibly welcoming. I had seen the city, had free board and lodging and, best of all, a shower. I was ready to launch into the next stage of my journey.

CHAPTER ELEVEN

The Train to Málaga

"It is all very well for savages to travel light, but not a bit of our precious luggage could we have spared – a box of medicines, a folding India-rubber bath, a basket of provisions, two or three parcels of books, a leather bag of sketching materials... an odd bag containing notepaper, opera glasses, passports, a teapot, a water bottle, and air cushion." – Mathilda Bentham Edwards

Next morning, despite the early departure of the train, Maria, laden with bags, also came to the apartment to bid me farewell.

"Ana, thank you so much for welcoming me into your home," I kissed her and she gave me a big hug. "I will send you a postcard from Ronda."

Lola, clad in a flowery housecoat and with rollers in her hair, repeated time and again *"ten cuidado"*, *take care*, and they all hugged me again, kissing me on both cheeks.

"Good luck, and take care with the bandits, child, perhaps you'll marry one."

They both roared with laughter. Maria loaded me up with food supplies.

"You must fatten up," she admonished me, waggling her finger, "or you'll never stay on that horse."

Off they went again into great peals of laughter. I got the impression that they did not take my proposed journey through the mountains very seriously.

The same dilapidated taxi drove me at the same reckless speed to the station, and I made the train with little time to spare. The carriages were packed and, with difficulty, I squeezed my rucksack and myself into a small space between a young soldier in uniform and a crinkled elderly lady with a basket full of eggs. It seemed that the holidays had arrived for the young National Service soldiers and the train resounded with their laughter, as they headed for their home towns. The air was permeated with the smell of garlic, stale sweat, and cheap Celta cigarettes. The strains of a guitar issued from a nearby carriage.

The timetable at Atocha station assured me that the journey from Córdoba to Málaga would only take six hours. But I had come to realise that such assurances regarding travel times in Spain were usually elastic. Gradually the train emptied as passengers reached their destinations and disembarked with relief from the claustrophobic carriages.

Later, in the sweltering heat of mid-morning, as we approached Bobadilla – a small village where all railways lines in the south of Spain seem to meet in one tangled web of metal – the train ground to a halt. Much gesticulating and shouting between the driver and the guard suggested that this was a serious breakdown. Worried heads appeared at the train windows. It seemed that we were there to stay. The temperature rose in the metal carriages, and there was no breeze to cool the exhausted passengers. Nothing moved on the sunburned plains.

By this time, I was alone in my compartment with a tall, thin man of forty or so. His brown skin was tightly stretched over his high cheekbones, his eyes were a faded blue and his hands were those of a farm labourer. He had not spoken since we left Córdoba and kept his head down and his gaze averted.

Something about him made me think he was foreign. Here was another chance to practise my Spanish, and satisfy my usual curiosity.

"Are you going to Málaga? I'm travelling to Ronda."

These innocuous remarks appeared to unsettle the man. He folded his hands over his chest in a protective gesture and seemed to sink further into his corner. I tried again, slightly louder. Perhaps he was deaf?

"I'm English, where are you from?"

After a furtive glance around to be sure that nobody was lurking who could hear him, he mumbled "No need to shout. I'm not deaf. My name is Janos, I came from Hungary. Many years ago."

"So is that where you are going now? Back to Hungary? It seems a long way round."

"No, young lady, I can never go back."

"Why, did you do something bad, something illegal?"

"No, or at least not as far as I am concerned, but my government will not see it like that. I came to Spain with many of my comrades to fight in the war against fascism. We were the freedom fighters."

"You were an International Brigader?"

"Yes, and I'm proud of it. Many of my comrades were killed on the Aragon front. One day I shared a foxhole with the nephew of your British prime minister, Winston Churchill. I think he survived." He permitted himself a small smile before continuing, "Strangely, many of the British were poets or writers – dreamers all of them. But we all had the same dream. We wanted to defend democracy. We failed."

"But the civil war ended in 1939 or thereabouts, didn't it? Why are you still here?"

"Why do you ask so many questions?"

"Sorry. I s'pose it's just my way. It does seem to get me into trouble. But I'm curious to know – I've never met anyone from the International Brigades."

Janos shrugged.

"Well, the Hungarian authorities are very right wing and several of my friends who returned home were shot or imprisoned. After all, we had fought alongside communists and that was frowned upon. So I stayed and worked on a farm in a small village in Aragon. General Franco offered an amnesty but I didn't trust him. I had no papers and if the *Guardia Civil* had found me I would probably have been shot. I met Angeles and we set up home together. For twenty years we were happy."

"Then what happened?"

"She died last year, of meningitis, and under Spanish law her brother inherited the house where we lived. I didn't trust him not to report me, just to make sure I didn't claim anything of hers, so I bought some false identity papers in Madrid. They belonged, by chance, to an Irishman who was killed in the fighting in 1938. There were many Irish and Scots in the Brigade. So, I'm heading to Málaga to see if I can find a ship to Ireland. I hear it's not too difficult to find work there."

"That's an incredible story. Have you no other family?"

"I really don't know. I had a sister, but of course I've had no contact for the last twenty years. We are of Jewish origin and I know that during the second half of the Second World War many Jews were deported from Hungary to some of the worst concentration camps, so it's entirely possible that she died." He smiled sadly. "We Jews are still persecuted wherever we are. Probably Ireland will be no different."

Janos lit a Celtas, and inhaled with a deep depressed sigh. It seemed the conversation was at an end.

***

The sweat was dripping down my nose.

"This heat is exhausting. Do you have any water?"

"No, I've run out."

My throat was parched. In desperation, I climbed down onto the tracks and approached the engine driver with an empty bottle and begged some water from the engine supply.

"*Estas loca!*" he replied – what madness.

With what sounded like dire warnings of instant demise if I drank the murky liquid, he filled the bottle and I retreated with my prize. He was right – a short time later my stomach was in revolt and I was very ill. I urgently needed to lie down. Sweating and dizzy, unable to stand up, I lay down on the uncomfortable seat.

Janos dozed in his corner. Neither of us saw the approach of the green clad *Guardia Civil* on their dusty bay horses. The first we knew of their presence on the train was when the door slid open.

"Documents," ordered the officer.

Janos leaped to his feet. I scrambled up, hoping against hope that I would not be sick over the *Guardia*'s uniform, and handed over my passport.

"Are you with this man?" Janos shook his head imperceptibly, whilst pretending to search for his passport.

"No, I'm alone."

"Why are you travelling alone?"

"I'm meeting friends in Málaga."

"It's dangerous for a young woman to travel alone. It's immoral." He scowled. "Sit down."

Janos had found his documents. Of course that was why he was worried. He certainly didn't look like an Irishman, but then the *Guardia Civil* wouldn't know that.

"Are these your documents?"

"Yes, officer."

Janos attempted a relaxed smile.

"You must come with me while I check them."

"What's the problem?" I asked "Why do you need to check?"

"Sit down and be quiet, young lady, or you will be in trouble. I thought you didn't know this man."

Janos seemed to crumple as he hoisted his rucksack onto his shoulder.

"See you in Málaga," I said in an attempt to cheer him up.

I leaned out of the window and saw, to my horror, that as he was led along the tracks, he was handcuffed with the officer's pistol pointing at his back. The second *guardia* followed with the horses.

"You can't do that, he hasn't done anything. He's innocent," I shouted desperately.

As the senior *guardia* turned towards me, a large hand suddenly covered my mouth. A voice in my ear said quietly

"Shut up, little blonde girl. Or do you want to die too?"

I struggled fruitlessly, only pausing when I noticed that the owner of the hand and the fluent English was dressed in the uniform of the Spanish Army.

"I've done nothing. Really. Let me go. What do you mean, die? Why should they kill him?"

"I get the impression that he is in Spain illegally and if so, he probably fought on the 'wrong side' in the civil war. If that's the case, he will be shot."

The senior *Guardia Civil* appeared in the doorway.

"You must come with me, *señorita*."

My legs trembled. I stammered.

"But I'm English. You've seen my passport. I don't know that man."

He grasped my arm.

"Come now, we'll have to see if that is true."

The soldier intervened.

"Corporal, as you will see, I am a lieutenant in the Spanish Army, and as such outrank you. What is more, many of my fellow officers are on this train. We will escort this young lady to Málaga and see that she gets into no more trouble."

The *Guardia* saluted smartly.

"My lieutenant, with respect I must refuse, my orders are to detain her."

"Then you will have to detain me and my fellow officers too, and I have no intention of walking all the way to Bobadilla. Please arrange transport for us all, and I will contact my commanding officer to advise him of our arrest by you and the reason for our delay in reporting for duty. Give me your name please."

Outnumbered and outflanked, the *Guardia* recognized defeat and reluctantly retired. No doubt poor Janos would pay for his frustration. I sat down heavily on the wooden seat and shakily wiped the sweat away with the back of my hand.

"Thank you. I had no idea they could actually arrest me just for shouting at them."

"They are very powerful. It was lucky I heard you. Now little English girl, tell me what you are doing all alone on a train, in the middle of Andalucía, accompanied by a criminal, and risking a firing squad?"

I told them of my planned journey on horseback and the story of Janos – there seemed no need to keep it secret now.

"Will they really kill him?"

"Yes, I'm afraid so, if they think he was involved in the War. As they see it, he came to Spain to kill Spaniards. He deserves to die. But he may be lucky and they'll just send him to work on the

Guadalquivir Canal. If he survives that, he will just be deported."

"Poor man. He can't go back to his own country or they'll kill him there. He was only following a dream."

"Yes, and he should have followed it in his own country, and left Spain to sort out her own problems."

I hadn't noticed just how handsome my rescuer was. Probably a little older than me, tall with curly dark brown hair and heavy brows. Good teeth and an amused expression. He gave the impression that rescuing damsels in distress was a day-to-day occurrence. Sprawling languidly on the hard train seat, he held my shaking hand. His comrades filled the carriage, cheering and reliving this small victory over the hated *Guardia Civil*.

Vicente, for that was my rescuer's name, offered to accompany me the following day to visit the city of Málaga.

"Just to make sure you don't get lost," he grinned. "Now, why don't you take advantage of this empty compartment and rest. And try not to get into any more trouble."

I fell into an exhausted dreamless doze.

Finally, in the late afternoon, a relief engine appeared from Bobadilla.

It was dark before we finally entered the claustrophobic tunnels that led through the mountains above the city of Málaga.

My nausea was abating and with the end of the journey in sight my spirits were rising. Due to the breakdown I had missed my connection, and there would be no train to Álora until early the next afternoon. I had plenty of time to explore Málaga with my handsome soldier. Maybe this would turn out to be another adventure.

Vicente helped me down with my rucksack and he and his friends escorted me to a cheap *pension* near the station. I took an inside room with a small window onto an interior patio: the price was lower than an outside room. The heat was oppressive. But I was overjoyed to find a shower with running water: it seemed clean enough and even the distant noise of the trains and the traffic couldn't keep me awake.

CHAPTER TWELVE

Málaga

"*Málaga, the enchantress, city of eternal spring, tranquilly bathing in the sea, shaded by the jasmine and the orange.*" – An unknown Spanish poet

"*Málaga is dirty, by no means pretty. The approach is mean and unprepossessing. It is a dull place celebrated for sweet wine and invalids.*" – George Denis

Vicente appeared at the *pension* in plain clothes early the next morning. He was still as good looking as I remembered, though the uniform was much more romantic.

"How did you sleep? Did you have nightmares?"

"No, I think I was just too exhausted. I really need a large cup of coffee, and I'm starving."

"Let's go into the city centre and find a bar. Do you like toast with garlic and tomato?"

"I'm not sure that my stomach is quite up to that yet. I'll just settle for the toast if you don't mind."

It was another beautiful clear morning with just a hint of a breeze from the sea. As we strolled towards the bridge we talked about Picasso.

"Did you know he was born here? He became a world famous artist and actually must have been very precocious. He said 'I never drew like a child; when I was twelve I drew like Raphael.' He was so difficult that his mother actually warned one of his wives that she was mad to consider marrying him. During the Spanish civil war he made his dislike and condemnation of General Franco obvious in his paintings. His belief that 'art emanates from sadness and pain' is clear in his most famous gruesome painting, *Guernica*, which shows the German bombing of the town in the north of Spain during the civil war.

"Look out," he grasped my arm as a cadaverous donkey and his even more cadaverous owner crossed the street in front of us. The donkey so over-laden with sugar cane that it seemed his poor skinny legs must buckle under the weight.

"I really don't know too much about Picasso's work," I said. "In Paris I spent a lot of time in the Louvre but I don't remember seeing any of his paintings."

"I can't say I am fond of his work but this one is very evocative of the attack on the unarmed country people. In 1937, the resistance from the republicans in the Basque country was proving a problem for Franco and his generals. In the town of Guernica was an ancient oak tree of great symbolic importance to the Basques, and it was decided to bomb the town on market day in an attempt to break their spirit. The German air force agreed to Franco's request and, for over three hours, dropped their bombs on the town. Fighter planes machine-gunned those fleeing to the countryside. The town was on fire and the flames could be seen fifteen kilometres away. The brutal attack on a civilian population inspired Picasso's masterpiece."

"Vicente, I'm confused. You're in the Spanish army, and General Franco is the 'Generalissimo'. So how do you feel about your side bombing all those innocent people in Guernica?"

Vicente was silent for a moment and I feared I had offended him.

"It's not simple. First of all bear in mind that I was a small child during the Civil War. My father was an officer in Franco's army but even he had his doubts. He obviously couldn't risk his family's safety by changing sides, but I think a lot of officers felt the same ambivalence as he did. And then after the war when I finished school, I had to find a job. The army seemed the obvious solution. After all, my family tradition was military and it wasn't too difficult for me to get into the military academy. I wasn't a very bright student. But I was on the 'right' side. Also, it was the German Condor Legion who bombed Guernica, not the Spanish. Now, enough of war. Come, let's find that breakfast you wanted."

***

The city of Málaga is built on both sides of the River Guadalmedina, though there was very little water in the river as we passed, and it seemed to be used largely as a rubbish dump. The vultures and crows circled overhead.

"Look, Vicente. There's even a dead donkey down there."

Covering our noses against the stench, we crossed the river by the modern bridge and I was agreeably surprised by the wide tree-lined avenue, the Alameda (so named because of the enormous poplar trees, *Alamos*), and the pleasant colonial aspect of the city.

We sat at a small café in the shade of the trees. The mirror-like sea was just visible and fishing boats bobbed sluggishly on it. London seemed so far away. I felt free and relaxed as the sounds and smells of the city enveloped me. Some of the young women, however poorly dressed, were quite beautiful, with perfect complexions and wonderful shiny black-blue hair. But the earlier travellers were divided in their opinions of Spanish women. Louisa Tenison commented on "their complete absence of beauty they soon fade, get flabby and bloated." Theophile Gautier was damning in his opinion of older Spanish women: "they have beards like mouldy cheese and moustaches like French grenadiers". Only Andros approved of their "dignified grace and expressive dark eyes, long oval faces, bright lips, a delicate nose and brilliant Arabian eyes."

Vicente was looking at me quizzically.

"What are you thinking about – you look so pensive?"

I laughed, "I was just thinking how much more alive Spain is than England. It's buzzing and so much more vibrant and colourful. I feel so at home here And I was remembering what has been written about the young women. I think they're lovely."

"They tend to get fat once they're married. Perhaps they don't need to try any more." Vicente was devouring his garlic on toast. "Do you know much about Málaga? When I first came here as a young officer I was very lonely. But it has grown on me. It's a beautiful city."

"I remember reading what Louisa Tenison said about the siege of Málaga by the Christian armies. She described the thousand white sails of Fernando's fleet of warships waiting offshore."

"I'm impressed by your memory and you know far more than I did when I first arrived," Vicente said with a smile.

"Yes, I had enough time on the train to digest a load of Spanish history.

The siege nearly ended in disaster when a Moorish fanatic crept into the camp intending to kill the young monarchs; however, he mistook the tent and wounded one of Isabella's ladies instead. Help did not arrive and the Moorish occupation of Málaga was over. It was too late for an honourable surrender and the brave commander, Hamet-el-Zegrí, was executed. In punishment for the prolonged resistance by the Moors, Fernando condemned the whole population of the city to death or slavery. Isabella would have been inclined to be more merciful but for the appalling state in which the Christian prisoners had been kept.

"You've obviously done your homework on the young Christian monarchs."

"I was in Córdoba with a couple of young kids who really knew their stuff. They told me about the city, and loads about the history of the Jews."

Vicente clapped his hands at the waiter for the bill.

***

Following the *alameda* with its colourful flower stalls, we headed for the market. The Arab-built Puerta de Atarazanas still forms the elegant entrance arch to the main market. Over the arch can be seen the motto of the Nazarite Emirs: "God alone is the Conqueror". It is a noisy old building crammed with stalls and colourful mayhem; it's divided into three high-ceilinged halls. Meat, fish and fruit are separated by archways, each trader outdoing his neighbour in proclaiming the freshness and cheapness of his wares. I recalled a description in a book by George Dennis who visited this market in

1836. He was entranced by the diversity of sound and colour "amidst this multitude of economically fragile people", huddled beneath the canvas awnings, which reminded him of enormous white bats with their wings outspread. "Respectable ladies seated on the ground surrounded by a veritable wall of baskets full of tempting fruit, where the colours mixed in a rich and dazzling contrast."

His description of economic fragility was even truer after the civil war. Whilst food now appeared to be readily available again, the poverty resulting from post-war inflation, amongst other causes, made all but the cheapest produce out of reach for many shoppers. Nothing, it seemed, had changed except that many of the "respectable ladies" now sold from stalls. The produce was the same: lemons, oranges, blue-black figs, cherries, peaches, apricots, almonds, and grapes. Mounds of coral-red sweet tomatoes ripened in the Andalucían sun, alongside peppers, strings of onions, and sweet smelling garlic; a kaleidoscope of colour and choice. The patient donkeys stood, head ropes dangling, their panniers full of green and yellow melons – the Spanish say that melons are like women, you cannot judge them by their appearance.

Close by, an old country woman, dressed in black with a headscarf to protect her from the searing sun, sat on a little stool surrounded by baskets of eggs, divided into white and brown.

Dizzy from the crowds and noise, and with my stomach still queasy from the train, a wave of nausea overcame me from the smell of blood at the stall selling fresh horsemeat.

"I have to get out of this heat. I feel sick."

Vicente looked at his watch.

"I have to go to an office here in the city. My horse Zocalo is arriving in the next few days from Madrid by train, and I must find out exactly when he will get here."

"Who looks after him? The journey must be awful for him in this heat."

"I think he'll be OK. My father is sending him with his own groom. Do you mind if I leave you for a while – you could go to the cathedral, it will be cool there. We could meet at the end of the Alameda. About eleven o'clock?"

"No problem. I promise I won't get into any trouble. You told the *Guardia Civil* you'd keep an eye on me."

To my surprise, he bent and kissed me lightly on the forehead.

"No chance. I don't plan on losing you."

What a shame – I met this gorgeous man and now I had to head off into the mountains. I wondered whether this was fate and if I should cancel the riding holiday.

Following the sound of bells, I headed in the direction of the cathedral. The spire was just visible through the trees and I passed gratefully through the massive side doors into the gloomy, cavernous interior. Built on the site of the *mezquita*, it was commenced in 1528 but only finished in the eighteenth century. One irreverent traveller described the building as a "pig with one ear". Another wrote "extraordinary taste, an immense pile of no great beauty, magnificent and clumsy," I agreed wholeheartedly with them. It had no atmosphere and very little to recommend it…

Small groups of worshippers knelt before the images in their chosen chapels, which were situated around the main nave of the impressive building. Candles were lit for the souls of those departed and the sweet overpowering smell of incense filled the slightly stale air.

The gardens were fragrant with roses, bird-of-paradise plants, and perfumed jasmine, and shaded by magnificent palms. I sat on a shady bench to enjoy the peace and quiet.

An elegantly attired elderly lady, dressed in mourning, smiled and asked permission to join me on the bench.

"May I join you?"

"Of course." I moved over to let her sit down. "Are you from Málaga, *señora*?"

"Yes, I was born here, but I live alone now that my husband and son are dead"

"I'm so sorry, what happened to them?"

She twisted her handkerchief.

"They were killed in the troubles. I come to the cathedral to hear mass every day and to pray for them."

She spoke quietly and looked nervously about her, still fearful of eavesdroppers and reprisals from Franco's spies

"Was the war bad here, for your family?" I asked.

I watched, horrified, as tears began to roll, unchecked, down her cheeks. Once again my lack of tact had caused tears and revived memories.

"I'm just curious about the war, I'm so sorry I upset you, please don't cry."

I fished for my handkerchief but it was grimy and I stuffed it back in my pocket.

But she seemed not to have heard me, she was deep in her memories.

"They came in the night. We were all sleeping," she whispered so I had to lean towards her and strain to hear.

"It was our neighbour, Ramon and his friends. They had guns and told my men to get dressed. When I tried to help my husband one of them hit me across the face." She ran her fingers down a faint scar. "There was a lorry waiting in the street and more men with guns. I recognized one of the prisoners in the back – it was Mercedes the schoolteacher – why were they taking her? My son tried to kiss me goodbye but they just pushed him down the stairs. I grasped Ramon's hand. I asked, 'Where are you taking them, Ramon – they have done nothing. We are your neighbours. Remember how I looked after your mother when she was ill. I beg of you not to take them.' But Ramon just looked away and ran down the stairs. I looked out of the window and saw the lorry accelerating up the street. I never saw them again, nor knew what had happened to them. I beseeched Ramon to tell me, every time I met him, but he said I, too, would disappear unless I kept quiet."

"How terrible for you," I whispered. "Do you have any other family?"

"No, I am alone. Now I must go or the mass will have begun."

She smiled at me sadly and touched my shoulder.

"*Adios, señorita.* Be happy."

She was so dignified in her grief; my heart bled for her loneliness.

***

The breeze was cool and, to delay the long hot walk back to the Alameda, I turned to Richard Ford's book. Known for its gentle climate, it appears that Málaga became a favourite place for well-to-do invalids to spend the winter months when the rest of northern Europe froze. However, most of the travellers who wrote of their visits to Málaga commented on its dullness and lack of interesting buildings, and indeed Ford commented that "the very dullness of Málaga benefits the invalid". Sufferers from lung disease or rheumatism flocked to the elegant hotels. One unfortunate traveller, Frances Elliott, was unlucky enough to visit Málaga when the hot north wind – the *terral* – brought swirling dust clouds and intense heat to the city. She reported that Málaga was "a terrible place. All sun, dirt, traffic, bad smells and disgusting dust."

But today, in the August heat, strident street vendors plied their trades: water sellers with large chilled terracotta jugs sold "*agua fresca como nieve*" – water fresh as snow; gnarled countrymen with straw hats carried buckets of prickly pears, which they peeled in buckets of water to wash off the tiny, irritating soft spines; others sold *horchata de chufa* – a thick milky drink made from tiger nuts, scooped out of earthenware jorums for a handful of small change; fish-sellers known as *cenacheros* with baskets or long ropes hanging from their forearms shouted baroque Andalucían chants offering fresh anchovies and live sardines; and a colourful gypsy woman sold fragrant jasmine flowers, with a child at their breast and the rest of the children hanging under ample skirts and only peeping out to clamour "*pesetas, caramelos*" "Pretty lady, give me money for bread" whined the mother, forcing a flower into my hand.

In Spanish towns the noise seemed overwhelming: cars, bus horns, rattling trams, emaciated horses drawing carriages with wheels rumbling on the cobbles, donkeys braying and being answered by companions, and the shouts of the street vendors. In the distance the cathedral clock chimed the half-hour.

The central avenue of giant trees gave welcome shade from the hot sun and the fresh breeze from the sea encouraged the wealthier citizens to pause at the pavement cafés, whence an endless murmur of conversation added to the clamour. In the shade of the trees the many flower stalls made a splash of colour and their perfume filled the air. Spain had a smell unlike anywhere else: a mixture of fried fish, stagnant drains, frying olive oil, garlic, sweet jasmine flowers, and a myriad of other indefinable ingredients that permeated the air and combined to create an unmistakable Spanish aroma. Whilst Hemingway rejoiced in the "sounds, the views, the taste and the sounds of Spain", one dissatisfied visitor in 1867, Matilda Edwards, complained that the "streets all smelled of fish – raw, fried, fresh, salted or stale".

CHAPTER THIRTEEN

The Civil War in Málaga

"Deep-seated are the wounds of civil brawls."
– Marcus Annaeus Lucan

Leaving the cathedral gardens, I had paused to ask an elegant middle-aged gentleman to direct me to the house where Picasso was born. To my astonishment this innocent enquiry provoked an irate reply.

"He's no son of Málaga."

I took a surprised step backwards as he waved his stick threateningly in my face.

"He's a communist, a red. He brought shame on us all."

Banging his stick on the ground, he muttered angrily to himself as he strode off down the street, as if fearing that he had said too much. Definitely a supporter of General Franco and his right-wing rebels.

As I returned through the city to meet Vicente, the results of the recent and bloody war were evident from the number of limbless beggars sitting in dim doorways on home-made invalid carriages, or crawling the streets searching for something to eat that day. Theirs was true poverty. They foraged through the piles of rotting fruit outside the central market. On the beach they would await the arrival of the fishing boats to snatch the small fry discarded by the fishermen as they cleaned their nets. The blind worked as lottery sellers, accompanied by a child guide, shouting their numbers that offered instant riches for the lucky buyer. Children dodged beneath the tables outside the bars to collect cigarette ends.

It seemed unbelievable that only a few years previously the streets of Málaga had seen so much internecine strife and yet today, in 1962, despite the poverty, it gave the impression of calm. It seemed a vibrant city, but the reality of post-war survival for the poor and unemployed was harsh. Republican sympathisers were still unable to obtain work papers and without work they faced starvation. The black market, two years of drought, the civil war and political isolation were the main causes of the poverty and misery for so many of the people.

Vicente was waiting at the agreed spot.

"Did you sort your horse out?"

"Yes, they say he should arrive at the end of the week. He has to travel on the goods train and that's even slower than the train we were on."

"Hey, talking of trains, I'm late – we need to get my rucksack from the hostel."

"I'll walk you to the station. Just to make sure you're safe, you understand."

"You're laughing at me again. What could possibly happen to me between here and the station?

But secretly I was delighting in his attentiveness. He took my hand, blatantly ignoring the rules about physical contact in public.

"How come we can hold hands when it's not allowed?" I nervously snatched my hand away. "I don't want any more trouble with the police."

Vicente laughed, "being an army officer has its advantages. And most of the *Guardia Civil* we're liable to meet are junior to me and wouldn't dare give me any trouble. Shame that we can't spend the evening in Torremolinos. There are some great bars."

"I really have to go, it's only for ten days. I promise I'll come back. How can I get in touch with you?"

We pushed our way through the crowds at the station, with only minutes to spare. As the train drew out, he pressed a piece of paper into my hand.

"Here's the phone number at the barracks. Just ask for Teniente Pitarch."

CHAPTER FOURTEEN

I Arrive in Álora

*"I will mount my horses who whinny in the stables and
I will travel to the plains and villages of dusty Spain."*
– George Borrow

The small, white village of Álora nestles in a fold of the mountains
some sixty kilometres above Málaga. Dominated by the majestic
El Hacho peak and looking out over the lush valley of the River
Guadalhorce on its way to meet the sea in Málaga, it was once an
impenetrable fortress. The ruined castle sits on a sheer rock face and
has protected the inhabitants of this little village from the various
marauding armies for centuries. Built by the Moors in the 9th and
10th centuries, it forms a natural observatory and a strategic position
at the head of the Guadalhorce valley that made it impregnable until
it finally fell to the Christian Kings in 1484. King Fernando had
acquired some artillery partly made in England and Germany, and
the ancient walls succumbed after eight days of onslaught by this
new weapon. After each battle, the losers were treated well if they
surrendered. The beautiful surviving horseshoe arch forms part of
the castle and is unique in the western world and I was excited about
seeing it for myself.

An hour after our departure from Málaga the train ground to a
halt on the single track that ran through Álora Station. I followed the
few passengers that alighted and walked across the tracks towards
the village. Surrounded by palm trees, stretching up to the cloudless

sky, with its walls a mass of tumbling bougainvillea and morning glory in a riot of purple and red, it was unlike any railway station I had seen.

With a loud whistle the train departed en route for Bobadilla and as it disappeared round the bend in the hills, I sat down on the only seat available and wondered what on earth I was doing here. I had abandoned a very promising friendship with Vicente, my stomach was still in a delicate state, I spoke a minimal amount of Spanish, and I had no idea of where the Marqués de Llomelini's house was. Since I had arrived a day late there was nobody to meet me.

I asked the station master for directions and he launched into a barrage of Spanish accompanied by hand waving. "*Arriba, Vale?*"

It was not OK, since I was none the wiser, but I understood that I needed to climb the steep slope to the village. I looked up at the ruined castle, the hedges of prickly pears and the sheer rocks surrounding the village, and sympathised with the poor foot soldiers of invading armies faced with such a daunting task.

I heaved my backpack onto my shoulders and began the long climb up the steep dusty track, through almond and olive trees. Giant cacti lined the path, and I was sure those were rats scuttling about in the thick spiky roots.

At last, sweating and berating myself for not at least attempting to phone for someone to collect me, I reached the village. Tantalizing smells wafted from tiny kitchen windows, and I realized that many hours had elapsed since my early morning breakfast with Vicente. I was starving. Perhaps there would be some lunch kept for me at the house. The narrow cobbled streets were lined with dark, cool doorways and brilliant geraniums adorned ornate wrought-iron balconies. It was siesta time; the village appeared deserted in the searing heat. Skinny dogs, their ears raw from ticks, lay sleeping in the shade and a plaque on the wall of the street called *Calle Ancha* told me that Cervantes, the author of *Don Quijote*, lived here from 1586 to 1593 whilst working as a tax collector.

I came into a church square with two sleepy looking cafés and tables set up under the leafy trees, where I found some swarthy old men in straw hats playing dominoes and drinking small glasses of black coffee with *anis*. This place couldn't be right – they were gypsies. Surely Antonio Llomelini, Marqués de Tabarca wouldn't live in this part of the village? I chose the youngest, who looked the least threatening, and asked for directions.

"Where can I find the Marqués's house?"

"Do you mean the Señor Marqués of the horses?"

This sounded promising. He waved towards a whitewashed house on the corner of the square with windows tightly shuttered against the afternoon heat and a heavy, intricately carved wooden door.

"Over there."

Whilst they all watched me in silence, I nervously approached the house. The door was thrown open by a tanned, blonde, blue-eyed man who I guessed must be in his early thirties. Are you Antonio – Marquis de Llomelini?

"Forget the title," he laughed "Welcome to my home, you must be Jill."

I was overcome with relief – I had arrived.

"We expected you yesterday with the other guests. Here, let me help you with your rucksack."

"I'm sorry, I should have called you. The train was delayed and I had to wait until today."

Simply dressed in an immaculate white shirt, impeccably cut jeans and handmade leather riding boots, my first impression was that he had air of melancholy and fragility about him. His English was better than my Spanish. I was sweaty and dishevelled and hoped I would have time to tidy myself before meeting the rest of the guests.

"Let me show you to your room."

With his black and white terrier Chico at his heels, he led the way.

As he guided me through I realised that the house was much bigger than it had seemed from the outside. The dining room faced the village square and led on to the summer patio shaded by a grapevine. To the side of the house was the big entrance door and access to the stables. We climbed up to the first floor where three bedrooms overlooked the square and up the top floor where there were four more bedrooms, a cosy sitting room, and bar.

The room Antonio showed me was surprisingly spacious and airy with cool red earthen tiles on the floors and scattered brilliantly-coloured Moorish rugs. The blue-washed walls, crisp white linen sheets, and white bedspreads completed the simple austere style. Pictures of horses hung over the simple iron bedsteads.

"I hope you don't mind sharing with Susan," Antonio apologised. "We're a bit short of space at the moment."

"That's fine," I reassured him.

Antonio showed me the bathroom.

"We have no running water, so if you want to take a shower tell Juan, the kitchen hand. He draws the water from the fountain in the square. He climbs on the roof and, when you're ready, he empties the water through a hole in the bathroom roof," Antonio grinned. "Don't worry, he can't see you." He showed me the lopsided washstand with a mirror. "Here's a bowl and a jug of water for you to wash."

Whoever said Spain's plumbing was different wasn't wrong. Even my bedsitter in Notting Hill Gate had had running water in the house.

Antonio talked enthusiastically about the water system. He was clearly proud of this setup.

"In summer this is not a problem, but in the winter the icy water makes showering very painful. Next year we hope to put a tank on the roof. It will still have to be filled with buckets from the fountain but it should be a great improvement."

I decided that to try and improve my dishevelled appearance with only a small bowl of water was probably pointless and anyway Antonio was hovering, waiting to take me to the group.

"Let's eat, you must be hungry."

He led the way downstairs to a large table set under the cool shade of the grapevine. A small group, obviously foreign, were already seated around a jug of sangria.

An attractive, plumpish blonde girl waved at me from the other side of the table.

"Hi, I'm Susan. Sorry I can't get out but I'm jammed into this side of the table. Andrew will get you a drink. That's John in the corner, and David and Laura."

We smiled and shook hands; we were to spend two weeks together. At first glance the group looked quite promising. Richard Ford's warning came to mind about choosing your travelling companions in Spain carefully.

Susan seemed very extrovert, with an easy laugh. Her freckles and slightly turned up nose were immediately attractive.

"Shift up, John," she pulled up another chair. "Here, Jill, come and tell me about your journey. What happened to the train?"

"How long have you got" I laughed. "What an adventure, or perhaps a series of adventures. I'll tell you about it later."

Andrew passed the jug of sangria and a clean glass.

"You look as if you need this, and we're a glass ahead of you. Shall we introduce ourselves. Who wants to start?"

A tanned, tall young man in his twenties leaned forward, elbows on the table, brushing his tawny hair out of his eyes.

"OK, I'll go first. My name is David and horses are my living. I've a job training young horses in Newmarket, but my other love is drawing animals. One of the reasons I'm here is to finish some drawings of fighting bulls in the marshes. They're such amazing animals, so powerful and almost prehistoric."

Susan shuddered theatrically, "Why are you so obsessed with those dangerous beasts?"

"They're only dangerous if you get them alone, in a group it's rare for them to attack. They weigh about 600 kilos each; they're really quite awesome. Antonio kindly lets me stay here in Álora if I give him a hand now and then, and I'll go down to the Jerez area to complete my drawings."

Unfolding his long legs he replenished our glasses. His clothes had seen better days, and compared with the elegance of Antonio, seated next to him, he seemed rumpled. But the faded jeans, well-worn riding boots, a much washed shirt and, as he leaned over me to fill my glass, the male odour of horse and sweat were deliciously attractive.

"Your turn, Laura."

She was pretty in a blonde chocolate-box way, with perfectly manicured nails and whiter-than-white teeth. I was not surprised when she told us she came from California.

"I came to Álora to improve my Spanish, but then I met David and we speak English all day," she smiled at him adoringly.

She didn't seem his type. Was that a small pang of jealousy I felt? I had only been in this group minutes and yet I seemed to feel very strongly about David.

Andrew spoke next. He was tall, slim and, I guessed, about forty, with an air of competence and military discipline. But his eyes crinkled in the corners, behind his glasses, and belied his appearance of severity.

"I was in the Royal Marines, did a twelve-year tour and saw service in some pretty ghastly places. It's the mindless violence that gets you down. I got wounded in the arm and decided not to re-enlist." He paused thoughtfully. "But perhaps I made a mistake – I just can't seem to settle in Surrey. I suppose it will take time, but patience isn't my strong point. I tried a job in Africa for a few years, but that didn't work out.

"Do you have a family?" asked Susan.

He shook his head. "No, my wife left me some years ago. She couldn't take my long absences, and I have to admit I wasn't the easiest person to live with when I was at home. Her friends were very irritating and she said I was rude to them. At the end we rowed the whole time. But enough about me."

He glanced round the table, seemingly embarrassed at his outburst.

"Yes, I'll warn you about Andrew," David broke the sudden silence. "He snores horrendously, or did last night, when we shared a room."

"Perhaps that's why my wife left me," laughed Andrew.

"Well, I do have a family," John suddenly interrupted, like a magician pulling a rabbit out of a hat. "But they're not at all interested in Spain. I'm a bird-watching buff and I'm really here to see birds of prey." He sighed with irritation, "But I hate this heat. I didn't realise how bad it would be, and the oily food plays havoc with my digestion." His bulging eyes, thinning hair and bad teeth were most unattractive. And I had guessed right – he was an accountant. We were soon to discover he had a very short fuse, and little pleased him. Despite his assurances of having been born in the saddle, he turned out to have the least experience on horseback of the group. His whining tone was instantly irritating. I flinched at his lack of tact and saw David smiling quietly at John's stream of complaints. Luckily Antonio didn't seem to have taken offence at his criticisms.

To defuse the atmosphere I turned to the pretty girl next to me.

"OK, Susan, your turn, tell us all."

"Well there's not really too much to tell. I'm twenty-five, and I help my parents on their farm. I'm just a glorified bookkeeper, which is so boring. I hope that this holiday may be a bit of an adventure." She pushed her sunglasses back on her bubbly blonde curls. "It just sounded different somehow. I was supposed to be getting married in six months time, but I've known Paul, my boyfriend, since we were kids and I'm just not sure I love him. I want to see a little more of life before I settle down. I've ridden all my life but I had a bad fall out hunting and lost my nerve a bit."

It sounded as if we were going to get on – at last I'd found someone else who understood the need for adventure.

Antonio smiled and turned to me.

"Your turn, Jill."

"I'm searching for bandits," I said, feeling a bit foolish and expecting the same derisive reaction I had received from Ana and Maria. "I know that there won't be any now, but it's not so long ago that they lived in these mountains and some of their stories told by the early travellers are fascinating. I want to ride the roads where they robbed the travellers and stay in the same inns."

Antonio raised his eyebrows in surprise at the mention of bandits and David laughingly explained about my search. Susan, at least, took me seriously.

"I think it's very romantic. And who knows, perhaps Jill and I will be kidnapped for a ransom."

I glanced at her gratefully for not making fun of my reason for being there.

"I hope your father's rich, Susan," I said. "I don't think my parents would pay to have me back at the moment."

"My mother would make him pay up, or he'd never hear the end of it."

To general laughter we turned our attention to the food.

Lunch was simple – local bread, dense and filling, and *gazpacho* – a chilled Andalucían soup made from tomatoes, cucumber, green peppers, bread, garlic and onions, finished off with a generous dash of olive oil and vinegar.

It was a meal in itself and perfect in such extreme heat.

"I read a story about *gazpacho*," I told Susan, "and about the bandit, José Maria El Tempranillo. He was hungry and thirsty, and visited a roadside inn. Some travellers were drinking *gazpacho* from a large bowl in the centre of the table, each with a wooden spoon. The bandit asked them politely if he might share their food. They refused, saying that they had no spare spoons. 'That is easily fixed' answered José Maria – and he took a piece of bread and, tearing out a hole in the centre, used it to scoop up the soup. Ignoring the travellers' protests he finished the bowl, and then identified himself, pulling out his pistol. Too late, they realised their error. 'Now you will do the same as I have to do,' smiled the bandit, 'eat your spoons.' And with that he swallowed his piece of bread whilst the travellers were forced to eat their wooden spoons."

"He was one of the *good* bandits wasn't he?" asked Andrew, mopping up *gazpacho* with a hunk of bread.

"Most of the stories seem to say he was polite and didn't kill unnecessarily."

I could sense that others in the group were not too interested in my enthusiasm for bandits.

Our meal finished with the sweet muscatel grapes, freshly picked from the grapevine that covered the and leafy patio. Replete with sangria and good food, drowsiness overcame me. Antonio pushed his chair back and rose from the table.

"I think we could all do with a rest. Let's take a siesta and later we'll ride. Why don't we meet at seven o'clock?"

It was too hot to think of any outdoor activity until some of the heat had gone from the sun, and a sleep was just what I needed.

William Clark reminds us that "in any foreign country the traveller ought to adapt the habits of the natives", and a siesta would be perfect.

I lay down on the bed and closed my eyes. I realised I was tired – exhausted. There was so much I had meant to ask Susan, but the next thing I knew she was shaking me awake.

"Time to ride. The others are waiting."

CHAPTER FIFTEEN

Our Horses

"It is impossible to behold anything more elegant, more noble and more graceful than an Andalucían stallion, with its stately head, sparkling eye and neck swelling out like a pigeon breast. It cannot be equalled for mountain travelling. Docile, patient, and intelligent, the best thing a rider can do is to let him follow his own impulse." – Théophile Gautier

We gathered in the cool hallway to be shown the stables. David and Laura were absent but I was too excited to meet the horses to let it worry me. These were housed in a long, low barn at the rear of the house, each with an individual stall. At the far end was a water fountain and an immaculate tack room with each horse's name over its saddle and bridle.

We were to take an evening ride through the orange groves to the mountains surrounding the village. The grooms led out the horses. Penelope Chetwode (in *Two Middle Aged Ladies in Andalucía*), who also rode with Antonio, described the Spanish horses as "decidedly odd. They had ewe necks, cow hocks and unusually straight pasterns."

"The pure Andalucían strain is descended from the Arab horse," Antonio said as he took the halter of a beautiful grey. Emir Abd el-Kader wrote of the Arab horse, "by reason of his elegance he resembles an image painted in a palace, though he is as majestic as the palace itself".

Susan stroked the neck of a showy black.

"They are beautiful. Are these pure Andalucían?"

"No" Antonio told her, "the pure Andalucían horse is heavier and not so sure on his feet as these Hispano-Arabs. This breed is safer on rocky surfaces and will fit easily between narrow rocks where the heavier horse can't go. They are perfect for this sort of terrain and very strong."

More than once, when faced with sheer drops and seemingly impassable rock faces, I remembered his advice and let my horse take his own route out of danger.

"There is a theory that horses have bigger eyes than other animals which enables them to be more conscious of danger." Antonio shrugged. "Who knows?"

Andrew looked as apprehensive as I felt.

"I've ridden a lot, but these saddles are new to me," I said nervously.

"I'm sure we will be fine," he replied, almost sounding convinced.

The *vaquera* saddles were magnificent with their thick sheepskins and the big iron stirrups. Although I had always loved horses, it had been at least two years since I had ridden and I wondered if I was mad to be undertaking such a journey. What if I couldn't keep up with the others? We were a motley crew.

Antonio exuded calm confidence as he said, "Jill, here, take Krishna, I think you'll get on well together. Pitirri!" He summoned a dark-skinned lad who was brushing down a grey horse. "Help Jill with Krishna."

Pitirri, the gypsy groom, smilingly helped me to mount and showed me how to hold the reins of the unfamiliar bridle. Krishna was a pretty chestnut with a white blaze down his face and three white stockings, which in England would have been unlucky. But he had wise eyes and seemed calm enough. He stood quietly and as the others shortened stirrup leathers and adjusted bits, I began to relax.

"Susan, you can try Platero, this grey."

He was a big horse, dark grey with an almost black mane and tail, and a nervous habit of throwing his head about. I was glad Krishna had no such traits.

"Don't take any notice" Antonio reassured her, "it's only impatience. As soon as we start to move he'll behave. Keep the reins loose in your left hand. The Spanish bit is quite fierce, so don't pull too hard."

Andrew was helped aboard Ligero, another chestnut.

"Don't worry" Antonio reassured him, sensing his nervousness. "He's quiet and very comfortable."

Antonio turned to John

"How well do you ride?"

"Pretty well," John smiled confidently, "I've ridden all my life." Antonio was holding Gitano, a stunning black with a flowing mane.

"See how you get on with this gypsy, then."

I wondered if he would be able to handle such a spirited animal.

Antonio took the reins of his favourite grey, Rondeño, and Pitirri was to ride Rosa, an ugly little grey mare with floppy ears. He gave us a hand up and adjusted girths and stirrup leathers.

"We wear the stirrups much longer than on an English saddle," Antonio explained. "It makes them much more comfortable for long distance riding." Certainly the large iron stirrups made mounting effortless and the sheepskin-covered saddles were like armchairs.

"Impossible to fall out of," said Antonio with a broad smile. "*Vamanos*," – let's go. "Hold your reins in your left hand only and that way you have your right hand free for emergencies and swatting flies."

Antonio pointed at Pitirri, whose horse, Rosa, had two plaits in her mane.

"He's just a superstitious gypsy," he grinned, "they think that a plait in a horse's mane will keep the evil eye away."

All the horses seemed to be well mannered and were very sure-footed as we rode through the village over shiny cobbles, to a cacophony of dogs and naked Murillo-like urchins scampering alongside. Nose in air, Chico superciliously ignored the barking street dogs but kept close to Antonio's horse for protection. My chestnut gelding was docile. He would be my companion for the next ten days over difficult terrain and I had to depend on his good sense to keep me safe.

"Why won't my horse walk, Antonio? He's doing a very uncomfortable jog," came the first of many complaints from John.

"Partly because he is excited to be out, but also because you're pulling at his mouth," Antonio told him patiently. "Be more gentle. Don't forget it's a much fiercer bit than you are used to."

With Antonio riding so elegantly and effortlessly at the head and two grooms, Pitirri and his young nephew Sebastian, bringing up the rear, we left the village, skirting the orange groves with their just-forming green fruit, and began the steep climb to El Hacho Mountain far above the village. Although the sun was still very hot, the air here grew cooler as we climbed. The view over the Guadalhorce River valley down to the city of Málaga was breathtaking. The world seemed alive with the shrill rasping of crickets, and the hoarse call of the bee-eater birds circling above us. White farmhouses were scattered over the hillsides on each side of the valley that was filled with splashes of colour from the pink and white oleanders, their roots deep in the sandy riverbed. Horses and mules were dotted along the islands left by the decreasing pools of water, grazing on the little remaining grass in the hot summer sun.

"That looks like hard work," Susan said and pointed to the village women who were hanging out their washing on the oleander bushes alongside the deep pools used to do the laundry. They looked up and waved as we passed. Despite the fact that it was August, the river still had a steady flow of water and at nightfall the goatherds would bring their flocks to drink before returning to their stables in the village.

"Look there," Antonio gestured. "Those are the griffon vultures. Can you see the ruff of feathers around their necks like a lion's mane?"

He pointed to a group of ten or more enormous black birds cruising on the thermals in the valley just below us.

"They keep the countryside clean of carcasses. If they are really hungry they even eat small cats or dogs if they can catch them."

The village animals kept a low profile.

I was filled with a deep happiness. The sun setting behind the blue mountains, a beautiful horse beneath me, the smell of wild thyme crushed under the horses' hooves and the raucous chant of the crickets, was a heady mixture.

Dinner was served at ten, when the air had cooled. After the plates were cleared away David, guitar in hand, entertained the party as we sat contentedly round the table in the cool patio. He played hauntingly beautiful Moorish melodies – songs passed down through the generations of musicians since the Moors first landed in Andalucía – tales of shepherds, bandits, impossible love and death. As I watched him bent over the guitar, his shaggy red-blonde hair covering his face, long fingers caressing the strings and eyes closed in concentration, I was surprised to feel a warm glow of attraction.

But Laura seemed proprietorial. Her hand on his knee conveyed ownership. "*He's mine – hands off.*"

***

"Don't you think David is drop-dead gorgeous?" I said as I spat toothpaste into the bowl.

Susan yawned. "He's not really my type. I prefer them dark and mysterious, but I can see what you mean. Sort of rugged but cuddly. He's probably got a wife and three children hidden away somewhere."

That possibility had not occurred to me.

"Well he didn't mention them, and in that case where does Miss California fit in?"

Susan laughed as she covered herself in anti-mosquito cream and climbed into the narrow bed.

"You really do fancy him, don't you. I don't think Laura will be too pleased. She's like the cat that got the cream. You may get scratched."

"Perhaps she's too perfect. Time will tell."

CHAPTER SIXTEEN

A Day's Ride

"The wind of heaven is that which blows between a horse's ears." – Arabian Proverb

The following day we rode on the other side of the river to the nearby village of Pizarra.

"Is Laura not coming?" Andrew asked Antonio.

"No, she doesn't like horses. I think she's a little scared of them. She's just here to learn Spanish."

"So she won't be coming with us to Ronda then?"

Andrew sounded disappointed.

"No, she'll stay here and keep going to Spanish classes in the village."

Susan winked at me.

"While the cat's away the mice can play," she grinned wickedly.

"What are you two plotting?"

I hadn't seen that David was riding close behind us.

"Just girls talk," Susan smiled at him. "We hear Laura won't be coming to Ronda, but David, you'll be coming won't you?"

"Yes, I've promised Antonio I'll give him a hand with your group."

We rode through vast fields of sugar cane, as high as the horses' heads, and splashed along the shallow river, where naked brown children played, shrieking in mock fear at the sight of the horses.

Once in the village, we left our horses in the stable at the inn with Pitirri and wandered the narrow streets of the old part of the village. We were becoming accustomed to the hordes of children who followed us, fascinated by these strange blonde women who wore trousers.

Lunch at the local inn consisted of "*caldo por encima*" – a delicious broth made with tomatoes, peppers, onions, garlic and potatoes, all fried together and poured over bread. We were all famished, so the large earthenware bowl of broth disappeared rapidly to be replaced with a large dish of crispy fried eggs with less crispy chips. We were to learn that Spanish chips always turned out to be greasy and soggy whereas the eggs fried in olive oil have wonderfully crisp lacy edges.

Later, in the early evening, we remounted, left the village and passed the threshing ground or *era*. This is a large round area inlaid with cobblestones, onto which the corn sheaves are placed for winnowing. Two horses are harnessed to a homespun *trillo* or sledge, with sharp metal or stones inset on the underside.

Antonio moved his horse closer to mine.

"The grain is separated from the straw and chaff by the sharp stones or metal pieces on the underside of the board," he explained.

We moved our horses upwind as they and we started to cough in the dusty air. More farmers brought their corn to be threshed and the scene resembled a country fair with carts arriving drawn by teams of mules and women wearing colourful headscarves and broad-brimmed straw hats. Over the phantom figures hung a pall of dust as the women repeatedly tossed the light yellow chaff against the wind. Cartloads of separated grain, chaff, and corn stalks were then driven away to be stored, the grain for bread, and the chaff and corn stalks for the animals. It seemed the picturesque scene that unfolded before our eyes could have been from the Bible.

As dusk fell the lanterns were lit and in the distance a guitar was strummed. Even though there was extreme poverty and hunger in most of the towns in Andalucía, here in the mountains, it appeared that there was sufficient food.

The sun set as we made our way home across the river.

***

The following day Antonio called us.

"Who would like to ride again this evening? You need to get fit and used to your horses before we leave tomorrow."

Andrew stretched and said, "I think I'll stay and read and write up my diary. I'm stiff from yesterday's ride, and my stomach muscles are killing me."

John was nowhere to be found, having gone out to take photos of birds. However, reluctant to miss a moment of this experience, I went in search of Susan.

"The others don't want to go, will you keep me company?"

"Of course. I hope I can ride Platero the big grey again," she replied, and the two of us made our way to find our horses. I decided to ride a smaller bay mare named Divertida and Pitirri good-humouredly changed the saddle and led her out for me.

To my joy, Antonio had confirmed that David wasn't married.

"But look out, he's got loads of girlfriends. You'll have some competition."

He had laughed at my downcast face, and was still smiling as he walked away. I didn't know whether to believe him, but it turned out that David was to be our escort that evening. Susan nudged me.

"Are you sure you want me to come along? I don't want to play gooseberry to you two love-birds," she winked conspiratorially.

I could feel the blush starting at my feet and rising to the tips of my ears.

"Shut up, he'll hear you. I hardly know him."

I kicked her, and pretended to tighten my girth, burying my scarlet face in Divertida's sheepskin saddle. With a wicked grin at my embarrassment, she led Platero out of the stable, meeting David in the doorway.

"Are you girls finally ready? We'll miss the sunset if we don't get moving."

He led out a big grey gelding, and swung into the saddle with ease, taking the reins from the gypsy groom.

We followed the train tracks out of the village, crossed the riverbed, and headed across the ravine to another range of hills. We looked down on the village laid out below us in the fold of the mountain with the majestic castle set on the promontory above. The golden eagles who nest on El Hacho were cruising on the evening breeze, in search of supper.

David squinted up at them in the bright sunlight.

"It is a favourite place for them to nest on the large flat rocks where they're safe from predators."

As dusk fell, the light over the mountains was tinged with colours so intense that, for a moment, it seemed the skyline was on fire. We sat on our horses, gazing as the purple light faded and in an instant the fiery pink and orange glow disappeared. A slender new moon appeared over the mountain peaks. I breathed a deep sigh of contentment – I was in love with Spain, and perhaps with David too.

Susan stood in her stirrups.

"Turn your money over in your pocket, it's supposed to double when you see a new moon."

We turned for home and the horses, keen to return to their evening feed, quickened their step.

At a bend in the track David stopped beside a bush with yellow flowers.

"Stop a moment, and I'll tell you a true ghost story."

We reined in the impatient horses.

"Well, the villagers say that the ghost of a cleric appears to travellers after dark on this track. The legend is that a soldier returning from a battle in Flanders in 1643 went to a fiesta in a neighbouring farmhouse. When he prepared to travel home, his friends attempted to deter him and told him of a mysterious ghost who accosted travellers after sunset. The soldier refused to be scared and set off on horseback. He duly met the ghost who told him that he was the soul of a cleric who had died in a state of sin. He requested the soldier to ask the villagers to pray for him so that he might rest in peace. For each prayer said they were to tie a knot in a broom bush which grew close by."

"What a creepy story," I shivered with a sudden chill. "Susan look, the bush is full of knots. I'm not going to risk meeting that unhappy man," and, dismounting, I quickly tied my knot. I then had so much trouble remounting a restless Divertida that David had to come to my aid and I scrambled inelegantly into the saddle. I muttered a quick prayer for the troubled soul of the cleric – in case he should decide to come back to haunt us, whilst the ever practical Susan scoffed.

"What a load of garbage. Ghosts don't exist."

Feeling slightly nervous of noises in the undergrowth and looking over my shoulder, I was pleased when the path levelled out and we could allow the horses to quicken their step. The lights of Álora sparkled in the distance.

After dinner of delicious chicken, chickpea and potato stew and large slices of watermelon, we were given our saddlebags, or *alforjas*, to pack for the journey. They were surprisingly deep so it was relatively easy to fit in all we would need for the next nine days. Any extra equipment could be carried by the two pack horses that would accompany us. The saddlebags hung over the back of the saddles and on the front each saddle were long leather thongs for tying incidentals such as cameras and spare hats. John found plenty to complain about.

"Where is Antonio? I have no room for my equipment. I must have more saddlebags."

He almost needed a pack horse for himself, his cameras, and books. Antonio appeared; he was his usual diplomatic self and Pitirri was instructed to make extra room on one of the spare horses to accommodate the extra weight.

At last I was about to live out my fantasies nurtured by the books of adventurers – the romantic travellers. This was the life I had dreamed of for so long.

CHAPTER SEVENTEEN

We ride to Ardales

"A riding expedition imparts a new life, takes the conceit out of a man for the rest of his life and makes him bear and forbear. All that was disagreeable fades from the memory while all that was pleasant alone remains and makes a man forget he has a liver. Escaping from the meshes of London we are transported into a new world." – Richard Ford

I woke early. It had been a hot and airless night. The mosquitoes had mounted several successful attacks despite Susan and I covering ourselves in the latest insect protection. A combination of dogs barking and cockerels welcoming the dawn made sleep impossible. I looked at my watch – seven o'clock. Should I look for Juan and ask him to draw some water from the well so I could shower? The house was silent as I made my way to the kitchen, barefoot. The staff were afoot and surprised to see me so early.

"Is there a problem. Couldn't you sleep?" Juana the housekeeper was concerned. "You shouldn't walk with no shoes. You'll catch cold."

"I love the feel of the tiles, Juana. Don't worry."

"Can I make you coffee?" She pulled me up a chair.

"No, I'll wait, thank you. I was really looking for Juan so that I could have a shower."

Juana instantly summoned Juan.

"Water, immediately, for the *señorita*. Hurry up."

"Go to the bathroom and Juan will take the water up to the roof. Call him when you are ready."

This required some organization. Getting the right amount of water to remove all the shampoo was a difficult operation. Badly timed and it could mean a long wait while Juan returned to the well for another bucket. The water was icy and despite the heat I shivered while waiting for the next bucketful to be launched from above.

The smell of frying filled the house. The local *churro* maker had set up his oil drum fryer in the square in front of the house. He piped batter from a large metal container into the hot oil, producing long thin doughnuts that could be hung on reeds, for ease of transport, like a doughnut necklace. There was a long unruly queue of children, each holding out his peseta for a few *churros*. We joined the queue and indulged in *churros* dipped in a cup of thick sweet chocolate. The result was amazing but rather indigestible.

After breakfast, we squeezed last-minute essentials into our saddlebags which were then loaded onto our horses. The pack animals carried other essentials such as spare stirrup leathers, horse shoes, John's paraphernalia, and our midday picnic.

We gathered in the stables, taking Antonio's advice and covering ourselves in anti-mosquito cream. Antonio and Pitirri checked girths and John fussed over his camera equipment which the pack horses were carrying.

"Take care with that. It's valuable – make sure it's safely tied on."

"For goodness sake, John, stop being such an old woman," Susan mocked him. "It's perfectly safe unless the horse falls over, which doesn't seem likely."

I recalled Richard Ford's advice on the correct gear for adventure travel: "a sash around the waist which sustains the loins and maintains an equable heat over the abdomen, a jacket of black sheepskin, a cloak or a striped saddle blanket", while in summer "the head should be protected with a silk handkerchief tied after a turban fashion which all the natives do, in addition we always lined the inside of our hats with thickly-doubled brown paper"

He also advises to protect the eyes with a pair of blue gauze wire goggles. The best remedy for dry eyes, he claims, is to bathe them frequently with hot water and "never to rub them when inflamed, except with the elbows". Having come unprepared with brown paper we had to make do with straw hats purchased in Álora.

"Hold Chico for me or he'll follow us," Antonio said as he handed a wriggling terrier to Juana and mounted Rondeño.

We waved goodbye to the staff and commenced our journey. As we left the village, heading west towards the village of Ardales, into unknown country, past herds of grazing goats and sheep, it did indeed seem like a new world.

We descended into the valley below the village, through gullies and dry riverbeds and across dusty wheat fields. It grew even hotter and, whenever we came across a stream, we stopped so that the horses could refresh themselves. Spanish horses are accustomed to drink whenever water is available, but Antonio called out a warning.

"Be careful".

"What did Antonio say?" called John from the back of the line of horses.

"Keep a close watch on your horse or he can suddenly go down on his knees," I called back.

"Look out, John," David shouted, but too late.

John's horse seized the moment and he, the saddle and saddlebags were suddenly deep in the water as the horse rolled happily. Luckily, he had his camera in his hand but the rest of his belongings were soaked. I was so busy laughing at John that Krishna decided to join in the fun and took advantage of my distraction. With a gigantic buck he pitched me over his head and I landed face down in the water.

"Shit," I gasped as I came up for air, "Antonio, I thought you said that nobody could fall out of these saddles."

"Serves you right for laughing at John," crowed Susan.

"Pitirri, catch Krishna before he goes any further" Antonio was trying to keep a straight face and look concerned. "Are you both OK?"

"More or less."

I was embarrassed and soggy, but unhurt.

John, with the reins looped round his arm, was sitting on the bank emptying the water out of his boots, as he looked ruefully at his soaked saddlebags.

"You see, I was right to worry about my camera equipment. Just suppose it had been in these bags. At least my glasses didn't fall off. I've broken my spare pair so that would have been a major disaster."

Only my pride was dented. Taking my boots off, I waded into the water.

"I'm fine, the water cushioned the fall. But my sunglasses seem to have disappeared."

Krishna put up no resistance when Pitirri discovered him, grazing a little further up the river bank and looking very pleased with himself.

"Let's stop for lunch and get everything dried out," Antonio suggested. "John's saddle needs to dry in the sun or it will make his horse's back sore."

We picnicked in the shade of a giant cork oak with the horses tethered nearby. A Spanish omelette of potatoes and onions, cut into thick wedges with lumps of peasant bread from the Álora bakery was followed by slices of sweet *piel de sapo* or toad skin melon.

David helped John unpack his wet clothes and books and laid them in the sun to dry. I rummaged for some dry clothes in my saddle bags and hung the wet ones from my saddle. In such intense heat they would be dry before we reached Ardales. We dozed contentedly in the shade, as did the horses. Not even the deafening metallic chirping of the crickets disturbed the tranquil scene.

After an hour Antonio got to his feet, brushing oak leaves off his still immaculate trousers.

"We need to get going, or it will be dark before we reach the village."

Pitirri and Sebastian collected up the remains of the picnic and helped us all to mount.

Some kilometres further on we crossed over the road leading to the village Carratraca, famous for its mineral baths. I had contrived to ride next to David.

"What's that smell? It's like sulphur."

"You're right. The village is built on sulphur springs."

David told us the legend of the elderly beggar, Juan Camison, who wore a long nightshirt since his whole body was covered in sores. The old man watched how the shepherds drove their animals into the pools around the springs, to cure their ulcers. Juan followed suit and was soon completely cured. He decided to build a chapel to the Virgin of Health, *la Virgen de la Salud*, now the patron saint of Carratraca. The chapel was built and Carratraca became famous for its mineral baths with curative properties.

We passed by a small roadside bar, with groups of cadaverous patients from the spa playing cards and convulsively grabbing at their winnings as if each game was their last.

I told David the story of Théophile Gautier, who described visiting a spa where the curative baths were taken in a giant clay jar buried two thirds in the ground, and he and his friend sat with their heads sticking out 'like pheasants in a terrine'.

He laughed, "I think the baths in Carratraca are somewhat more modern."

Crossing through olive groves, we marvelled at some of the gnarled trunks, grown into fantastic shapes of gigantic proportions, probably at least 500 years old. Vines, almonds and yet more vines struggled for survival in the dry soil.

At dusk we crossed the low plains towards a village that lay sprawled against the blue-tinged Ronda mountains, with the castle ruins and a church perched on a rocky outcrop.

"What a magical sight."

Even the usually dissatisfied John was enthralled at the stunning sight of Ardales against the glow of the setting sun.

"That's incredible," David reined his horse in. "If you painted a sunset like that, nobody would believe the colours. Look at that orange cloud over the mountain there."

It reminded me of a description from a book by traveller to Ronda, called Adolphus Leycester, who wrote, 'The sunset glowed red over one of the barrenest sierras as I ever saw, and the whole hill seemed to be burning hot'.

The raucous calls of the frogs from the river filled the evening air and the little owls, *mochuelos*, were practising their *kieu-kieu* calls. Our dusty cavalcade climbed up the steep main street of the village, seemingly accompanied by every child and dog in Ardales, exuberantly demanding *pesetas* or *caramelos* – sweets.

"I can't wait to get these wet boots off," John groaned. "They have definitely shrunk."

"You'll probably need to get Pitirri to help you pull them off."

Andrew said unsympathetically "I'm heading for a cold drink."

It had been a long day and we were sore after so many hours in the saddle. But it was to be my first experience of sleeping in a *posada*. I was at last on the trail of the famous travellers and the bandits.

CHAPTER EIGHTEEN

The *Posada* in Ardales

"A posada *is a large room which serves a double purpose – one end for culinary purposes and the other as a general rendezvous for mules and asses and a perpetual dunghill to swarms of fowls."*
– George Dennis

The *Posada del Conde*, or Count's Inn, was situated in the main square. It was a long low building with a large arched entrance for travellers on horseback, carriages or the muleteers with their long trains of animals. Inside the arch was a big cobbled patio, with a drinking trough on one side. To the rear of the patio was a long stable already occupied by several mules and horses that were tied to rings in the mangers. Room was made for our horses; it had been a long day for them too.

Most of the writers who had visited such places complained bitterly about the armies of fleas, foraging parties of ants, and voracious bed bugs. Louise Tenison bemoaned the "industrious, unwelcome companions, not light active creatures which hop about, but a steady and determined array of slow creeping things advancing gradually and tranquilly".

Walter Starkie called them "the merriest fleas in the world, deserving the epithet of Flamenco".

Jose the *posada* owner was as short and skinny as Prudencia, his wife, was buxom. Due to his marital infidelity there was armed warfare between them and it was obvious to all that he was in the dog-house. Antonio whispered that José had been dallying with the servant girl for some eight years.

Prudencia was dressed in the customary floral smock so beloved of village women and all apparently made in one size, varying only in the brightness of the colours. She also clearly wore the trousers in their marriage and, standing in the massive doorway, issued a stream of ear-splitting commands to grooms and kitchen boys.

David and Pitirri were struggling with John's wet boots and Andrew had wandered out into the village.

"Susan, come with me, let's have a look inside," I wanted to see if the kitchen was as rustic as the early travellers had made out. I was not disappointed. Solid wooden beams served not only to support the roof but were used for storage of every type of vegetable: strings of garlic, red peppers and onions hung drying around the large room. Long wooden tables and benches filled the room and a veritable Noah's ark of chickens and cats were perched on all available surfaces. In the corner, barrels of what appeared to be wine were stacked haphazardly and pitchers of olive oil stood on shelves. In the heat of an August evening the temperature was sweltering as a big cauldron of soup simmered over the olive wood fire. Whatever the temperature, the muleteers would expect a hot meal.

"I really have to go to the toilet," Susan clasped her stomach in a sudden spasm of pain. "I hope it's not too far."

We went in search of the toilets and met Andrew on our way.

"Ye gods, what is that ghastly smell?" Andrew muffled, covering his face with his hands.

We need not have worried, the toilet was easily located by the appalling smell from the open drains. In a corner of the patio was a small shed. Smell or not, Susan had no choice and raced for the door, only to reappear some time later looking very pale.

"Don't go in there unless you really have to. It's awful."

This was our first experience of *posada* life and we were yet to learn the complexities of *posada* plumbing. The most usual was a unisex facility consisting of a wooden board with a hole in the middle. Underneath was a hole and a foul smelling ditch where chickens and rats picked at the choicer morsels.

The stable floor was covered with many years of chaff from the mangers, manure from the many animals who had passed through, and a certain amount of human manure from travellers whose stomachs had balked at the very rustic sanitary arrangements of the *posada* toilet. There was always a queue, so it was much easier and less odorous to use the stable floor.

The washing facilities consisted of a jug of water beside a tin or china bowl in the bedroom. Each room was often shared by three or four travellers (males and females were strictly separated) and washing was usually a fairly cursory affair. Since water was in short supply, and had to be drawn from the local fountain or pulled from the well, it was strictly rationed. Sometimes a small tin jug was supplied to encourage only a small quantity of precious water to be used. Susan and I found that trying to wash one's hair in a *posada* washstand required a considerable amount of dexterity. Since we two ladies occupied two beds in the four bed dormitory, we hoped that no more travellers would be squashed in by Prudencia and José to make a greater profit on the room. It was a pretty room with a balcony onto the village square. In most *posadas* it was necessary to pass through one room to the next, which made stripping off a nerve-wracking experience. One never knew if a stream of hairy muleteers or a travelling priest would suddenly trek through the ladies' bedroom on the way to their sleeping quarters.

"We ought to buy a padlock," said Susan. "What happens if the men need to go out to the toilet in the night?"

"I thought you were here for adventure," I teased her.

We had little luggage so unpacking wasn't a problem, and anyway there was nowhere to hang anything. My wet clothes had dried during the afternoon's ride.

When we met up with the others, we found that Andrew and John were sharing with a young man who seemed to be the Andalucían version of a travelling salesman. As usual John was moaning, this time about the lack of privacy.

"Surely they can find him somewhere else to sleep, it's cramped enough anyway with just two of us. The horses have better accommodation. Their stables are airy and comfortable. The mattresses are hard, the pillows are long and lumpy. I don't know how you expect me to sleep on what appears to be a sack of potatoes."

Prudencia could not be moved on the issue. There were no other rooms.

"What is in the mattresses, David?" asked Susan. "They *are* very lumpy."

"It's sheep's wool. That's why it's so heavy. But this is one of the better *posadas*. You know the poet, John Betjeman? His estranged wife, Penelope Chetwode, stayed here and she wrote in her book, *Two Middle-Aged Ladies in Andalusia,* that in the Ardales *posada* there were no bugs or fleas and all was scrupulously clean. She had been told that the walls were whitewashed each year, effectively killing off the local bug population."

Seeing that his speech had not had the desired rousing effect, David continued, "In other *posadas* the rooms are next to the horses on the ground floor, but in the case of Ardales we are on the first floor – it's much quieter."

I wasn't convinced and reminded him that an American traveller, Abel Chapman, aptly concluded that a *posada* was "a stable for beasts with an extra stall for their riders", and that George Borrow wrote "the hogs grunted, the mules screamed and the muleteers snored most horribly."

By the 1960s, there was electricity in most villages, but the only evidence of this was usually one very dim light bulb. Reading was almost impossible when night fell, but we were all too exhausted and hungry to care after so many hours in the saddle.

By custom, travellers would bring their own food and cook it on the communal stove, but in the bigger *posadas* food would be ready for those who could afford to pay. The cooking was done on an open fire in the kitchen next to the stables. Big stews of vegetables, chickpeas, lentils and potatoes were the order of the day, brewing gently on the charcoal or straw fire. Sometimes a lump of pork belly or a pig's ear lent flavour and rancid ham bones made a surprisingly tasty soup.

We made our way to the little dining room behind the kitchen.

I am normally quite adventurous but one thing I was dreading was *gaspachuelo* – a watery soupy base with lumps of soggy bread, potatoes and sometimes mayonnaise. The crowning glory was an underdone egg poached in the soup with raw olive oil poured on top. I had read that this soup was much favoured by *posada* cooks for its filling properties and relatively low cost. An early traveller described *gaspachuelo* as:

> A thick pasty substance in a huge copper cauldron. As far as I could ascertain, bread sodden in hot oil formed the foundation of the mess, to which garlic moreover lent its odours. The surface was garnished with poached eggs.

We were lucky. Prudencia had prepared a delicious soup made of ham bones and what appeared to be pieces of chicken. Louisa Tenison wrote of her suspicions that what appeared to be chicken was probably one of the village cats. I pushed the pieces of meat around my plate in an attempt to identify it.

"What's the problem?" inquired David.

"Nothing at all, I was just thinking how delicious the meat was and wondering if it was chicken."

He raised his eyebrows, but his attention was diverted by the appearance of Prudencia bearing a large plate of *jamón serrano*.

"This ham is cured here in Ardales," she told us proudly. "When you have eaten, José will show you our pigs and his store room."

Replete with good food and rough village wine, we followed José to the patio behind the *posada*. In a low stone building hung four ham legs.

"That's all that is left of last year's pigs," he said with regret. He led the way to a dark smelly stable, where four large black pigs snuffled amongst slops in a trough.

He explained that most country families have a couple of pigs. This accounted for the distinctive smell of pig which we had noticed permeating all the villages. Traditionally, they are killed in the autumn when they are fat on acorns.

"We let the pigs out every morning," he told us. "All the village pigs graze out together on the acorns round the village. At night there seems to be some sort of signal and they all set off at a gallop back into the village, each into his own stable. They don't stop for anyone, so if you get in their way you're liable to be knocked down.

"The pigs are our pets, but when they are fat enough they are slaughtered. We call it the *matanza*. The whole family and even the neighbours help. It's an important day for us. If the pig is good and fat we can have enough meat for several months. The kitchen is full of steam and chatter as water boils in cauldrons to cook the rice for the blood sausage, vegetables for the sausages are fried in enormous pans of oil, spices are pounded, and garlic is peeled and chopped.

Every piece of the pig is used and most of it – sausages, preserved ears and feet, blood sausage with rice or onions, lard and ribs – is stored for the long winter months. Salting is the most common method of preserving the meat. The legs and shoulders are used for the making of *jamón serrano*. The hams are either soaked or massaged with coarse salt and then hung to dry. The quality of the ham depends not only on the skill in the salting but also on the climate in which it is cured. Pigs that have been fed exclusively on acorns are said to have the best taste."

José smiled proudly and added, "To produce a tasty ham we need damp and cold weather, and in mountain areas this is no problem. All a good ham needs is air, salt and time."

Our first night in Ardales was memorable for its discomfort – the unforgiving horsehair pillows and lumpy mattresses stuffed with wool gave no quarter and we crawled from our beds the next morning saddle-sore and feeling much the worse for wear.

The local cockerels seemed to have no idea of when daybreak occurred and crowed all night in the light of the moon.

"I think we're all mad to be doing this. Another night like that and I'm going home. And to think that we're actually paying good money," John said as he dropped his saddlebags to the floor with a crash.

"Where's your sense of adventure? We have come to Spain

because it is different, old fashioned and romantic. We can't have it both ways." Susan too was unusually snappy this morning. David and Antonio seemed none the worse for the noisy night and disappeared to the stable to check out the horses. Andrew was out in the village, photographing a herd of goats.

Breakfast was bread toasted over the fire with olive oil and a clove of garlic with which to rub the oil into the bread. The milk for the coffee was served by the local goatherd at the door of the *posada*. The drumming of cloven hooves on the cobbles and the sound of the bells carried by the lead goats heralded his arrival. He squatted amongst the herd and squirted the warm goaty liquid into the metal containers that Prudencia handed him. The only alternative was a tin of Nestle condensed milk.

A far cry from cornflakes and cow's milk in Notting Hill Gate.

CHAPTER NINETEEN

We ride to Campillos

"I travel to make a dream come true quite simply, or to change skin, if you like." – Théophile Gautier

Although memorable for the discomfort, our first night in a *posada* brought me closer to my ambition – to ride in the footsteps of the famous romantic travellers. Ardales figured on the routes of most of those that journeyed from Ronda towards Córdoba or Málaga.

"*Adios,*" we bade farewell to José and Prudencia and, scattering small children as we passed, left the village en route for the lakes of El Chorro and the famous gorge.

Our route out of Ardales took us over the Roman bridge of La Molina, through increasingly rugged tracks and, as we left behind the gentle slopes and terraces of vines, pomegranates and carobs, we were exposed to the burning sun.

Susan was sunburned from the day before, even though she had used sun cream.

"It looks like I'll peel now. I just don't go brown. I even burn at home in the summer, so after a week of this sun I'll look like a lobster."

We rode through a patchwork of fields of stubble with horses and mules grazing, hobbled in their front feet to deter them from roaming. A few kilometres further on we came upon the first of the lakes, which was surprisingly turquoise in colour due to the reflection of the sky and, Antonio told us, to the high quantity of sulphur in the water.

"It smells even worse than Carratraca," John wrinkled his nose.

Egrets skimmed the surface and the pine trees were reflected in the water along the banks. A little whitewashed farmhouse stood beside the water with a trellis of grapevines shading the windows from the sun. Brown and ochre fields stretched away into the distance with two lone farmhouses and a wind-scorched tree.

As we rode Antonio told us about El Chorro.

"The lakes we are going to are three kilometres long, and there is a very deep narrow chasm through which the Guadalhorce river flows. The workers built a wooden and rope walkway the length of the gorge.

"Is the walkway very high up, Antonio?"

I was really bad with heights.

"I'm sure David will hold your hand," Antonio smiled broadly.

"Did I miss something, are my ears burning?" David asked, kicking his horse forward.

"No, it's just that Jill needs somebody to hold her hand on the walkway."

"It's a bit narrow but there is a rope handrail you can hang on to. We'll tether the horses and Pitirri will keep an eye on them. Jill, you don't have to walk along the gorge if you don't want to. It's very spectacular and it would be a shame not to see it, but you can stay with me and Pitirri if you're nervous."

"Come on Jill," Susan encouraged me. "Didn't you want adventure? David will look after you."

Fifteen minutes later we reached the end of the gorge.

Reluctantly I dismounted, and handed the reins to Pitirri.

"OK, but it looks horribly high."

David held out his hand. "I won't let you fall, I promise."

Antonio was helping Pitirri tie the horses in the shade of an olive tree "Be careful where you walk there are lots of adders here in the dry earth. It's a good idea to tuck your trousers into your boots."

The walkway was as impressive and as stomach-churning as we had heard – flimsy boards suspended from the sheer rock face by ropes.

I looked down at the water rushing over the rocks far below us, and tried not to panic.

"David, don't let my hand go. Andrew, please walk in front of me, it's very wobbly."

"It's perfectly safe," John dismissed my fears and pushed rudely past us.

"Look out, you idiot," I panicked as the flimsy wooden path swung on its ropes and rocked under John's weight.

"What are you doing you fool?" cursed David, as he held out his hand to steady me.

"Look, it's lasted for years, there's no reason for it to collapse now." John snapped as he climbed on confidently towards the middle of the gorge.

"It may not collapse, but I've read that quite a few people have fallen off and been killed," called Susan from behind us. "What an idiot he is."

I hardly dared look down at the river. The walkway had been built to enable materials to be carried from one end of the lake to the other and had taken seven years to complete. At the narrowest point the gorge is only three metres across from one side to the other, and David told us that he had seen mountain goats defy gravity and leap the ravine.

"Look on that ledge, see the vultures' nests," John said, in his element.

I kept a tight grip of the rope handrail and David's hand, and was very relieved when we heard Antonio shout.

"Time to go. John, that's far enough."

"With a bit of luck he'll fall off," muttered Susan, as we cautiously made our way back to the end of the gorge. "Andrew, give me a hand please, I'm beginning to agree with Jill that this is too high for me. But I'm glad I saw it."

Back on firm ground, we rested in the shade, waiting for John to return.

Antonio sat apart from the group and appeared to be in a sombre mood.

***

The smell of cooking reminded us that it must be lunchtime.

"Antonio, I'm starving, can we stop to eat?" Andrew got to his feet, brushing the leaves from his trousers. "John can catch up with us."

Susan and Andrew headed off on foot for the little bar alongside the lake, leading their horses, and we followed, leaving Pitirri to wait for John's return.

"A drink and a *tapa* is just what we need," Susan declared.

"Do you know what a *tapa* is?" asked Antonio. "One of the theories is that the word originated from the muleteers. As soon as they arrived at a bar they were served a pitcher of wine whilst they unharnessed the mules. So much wine on an empty stomach caused too much drunkenness amongst these gentlemen of the road so a law was passed making it obligatory to offer a small amount of food with each glass of wine."

"I thought that it was called that because the food was used to '*tapar*', or cover, a glass of wine so that the flies couldn't fall in," David said.

"Who knows," laughed Antonio. "There are many versions – take your choice."

Whatever the origin of the word, this bar produced excellent *tapas* of pork in a yellow almond sauce, and slices of potato omelette.

John had arrived and refused to eat.

"If you saw the flies in the kitchen you wouldn't touch the food. You'll probably all be ill."

"All the more for us," replied David, losing patience with John.

With hunger pangs satisfied, it was time to resume our journey towards the village of Campillos. We retrieved our patient horses and rode on. Climbing the pine-clad paths beside the lake, we came to the summit and paused to rest the puffing horses. Looking across towards Álora we could see, fringed by sharp peaks sitting deep in the valley, an exquisite little tributary of the main river with the opalesque colour of turquoise.

Riding along the banks of the lakes, a flock of Greater Flamingos rose above us like a pink cloud, on their way to their feeding grounds in the lakes of Fuente de Piedra a few kilometres away.

David squinted up at the noisy flock. "There must be thousands of them."

John was snapping away with his camera. Surrounded by so many birds he was, for once, contented and had forgotten to complain.

Kingfishers swooped across the water, a flash of turquoise and russet, in search of the myriad of red dragonflies zigzagging among the bulrushes.

As we rode towards Campillos the church spire was visible from several kilometres away, with its blue and white Moorish tiles glinting in the evening sun. Fields of sunflowers with their faces turned down in the evening sun alternated with rich golden fields of ripening corn.

As usual, a crowd of urchins accompanied us on our entry into the village down narrow cobbled streets with elegant wrought iron balconies. The *posada* was situated in the main square, and we rode through a large archway into the cobbled patio. The inn was in need of a coat of whitewash and at first impression looked uncared for. But when we met our hosts we realised that they had problems.

The *posada* was run by Manolo and Maria. He was several years older than her and very overweight. Since Maria had had both legs amputated, due to a childhood illness she told us, it fell to Manolo to struggle up the stairs to show us to our quarters. The bedrooms were, if anything, more spartan than those at Ardales.

Although it had been an easy day's riding we were all glad to hand over our horses to Pitirri, and keen to collapse with a cool drink in the shady patio of the *posada*.

"I really need a beer, my wet saddle is killing me," groaned John, as he sat down gingerly.

The thick sheepskin cover hadn't dried out after its dousing in the river the previous day.

"I think I have got blisters on my backside."

"Why don't you get Antonio to ask Pitirri to take the sheepskin off the saddle and dry it by the fire," suggested the ever-practical Susan. "If you get bad blisters you'll really be in trouble. I'm going upstairs to wash off some of the dust. Are you coming, Jill?"

IBERIA IN 910

OVIEDO

LEON

KINGDOM OF NAVARRA

PAMPLONA

KINGDOM OF LEON

AUTONOMOUS MOORISH STATES

ZARAGOZA

COUNTY OF BARCELONA

BARCELONA

AL-ANDALUS

TOLEDO

MERIDA

VALENCIA

UMAYYAD EMIRATE

CORDOBA

GRANADA

SEVILLA

MALAGA

☐ CHRISTIAN STATES
▨ ISLAMIC STATES

IBERIA IN 1150

FRANCE

SANTIAGO DE COMPOSTELA

KINGDOM OF NAVARRA

BURGOS

PAMPLONA

KINGDOM OF ARAGON

VALLADOLID

ZARAGOZA

BARCELONA

KINGDOM OF PORTUGAL

KINGDOM OF CASTILLA

TOLEDO

VALENCIA

LISBON

AL-ANDALUS

CORDOBA

SEVILLA

GRANADA

☐ CHRISTIAN STATES
▨ ALMOHADS

Students travelling with muleteers

Ronda Gorge and bridge

Smugglers in the Serrania of Ronda

Gipsies in Sacromonte

Map of my ride through Andalucia

Windmills of La Mancha

Garroting of a bandit

We took our saddlebags up to the little room we were to share under the roof.

"If there's one thing I will remember from this trip, it's the pillows," grumbled Susan. "I don't think my neck will ever recover."

We checked out the mattresses and they were definitely even lumpier, if possible, than the previous night, but seemed clean enough. I threw myself on the bed, tired after so long in the saddle.

"What's that noise?" Susan asked as she tested her bed. "The mattresses are made of leaves of some sort and they crackle. It will be a noisy night. Lucky we're not planning on any hanky-panky. Or are you?"

"Chance would be a fine thing. What with Miss California in the background and not being able to be alone with David, there's no way. But I'll keep trying."

"But Miss California is back in Álora doing her Spanish lessons." Susan grinned wickedly.

"Which gives me a few more days more to work on David without her interference. Don't worry – I'm making progress."

Susan sniffed sceptically. "Pretty slow progress if you ask me."

"You just wait and see. 'How poor are they that have not patience'. Shakespeare's Othello said that."

Susan looked unimpressed. "But Horace said '*carpe diem*' – seize today," she quoted smugly.

"OK, I laughed, "I give in. I'll take your advice. But if he runs a mile you're to blame."

The strings of onions, hanging up to dry, decorated our room as usual, but the smell was diluted by the cool evening breeze that came through the glassless windows. We splashed off some of the dust, and unpacked our crumpled clothes.

As we went down the steep stairs, intending to head for the nearest bar to quench our thirst, we had our first encounter with the forces of order, the *Guardia Civil*. These green-clad, sombre, threatening keepers of the peace wished to see our papers and those of the horses. Each horse was required to be identified as to ownership, age and colour. The officers' flat-backed patent leather tricorn hats didn't leave their heads as they solemnly examined our passports, and ourselves.

"*Casada?* Are you married?" barked the older of the two as he perused Susan's passport.

"Why does he want to know that, Antonio?" Susan frowned. "I'm not, but I don't see what it has to do with him."

Andrew whispered in her ear, "You're blonde. I bet he thinks you're one of those promiscuous Swedish girls he's heard about on the coast."

Antonio motioned him to silence. The police were too powerful to trifle with and if they thought we were making fun of them we could be in for trouble.

He explained to the *guardia* that we two girls had our parents' permission to come to Spain and ride to Ronda escorted by him, our cousin. Unconvinced, but with no good reason to detain us, they made a show of minutely examining the rest of the passports. After a few anxious moments they decided we didn't present any threat to the citizens of Campillos and dismissed us with a goodbye, "*vayan con dios*", before proceeding with measured tread to the stables with Antonio to examine the horses and their papers. We all heaved a sigh of relief and made our way out to visit the village for a brief stroll before dinner.

In the cool of the evening black-clad old ladies sat in doorways crocheting and gossiping, decorously facing inwards to avoid the eyes of any disrespectful men who might look at their stockinged legs. A donkey cart clattered down the main street driven by a sun-dried farm worker in a black shirt with an elderly white-haired lady sitting on a wooden chair in the back of the cart. She rode with dignity, looking neither to the right nor the left but when she saw us looking at her she turned away, pulling her black dress more tightly across her knees.

Across the square from the *posada* was the church, Nuestra Señora Santa Maria del Reposo. The magnificent baroque façade was carved from stone weathered by wind and rain to a beautiful soft pink. It seemed to have survived the destruction of churches during the civil war intact. We entered by the massive wooden doors over an impressive marble step, worn thin in the centre by many hundreds of thousands of feet. Evening mass was in progress and we stayed a while to listen to the soft tones of the organ and the responses of the small group of elderly faithful.

Hunger made us retrace our steps to the *posada* kitchen where the table was set with a large earthenware bowl of *porra campillera* made from fresh breadcrumbs, olive oil, tomatoes, red peppers, and garlic. Tuna fish, olives and little squares of *jamon serrano* were laid out in little bowls. The ham was a bit chewy and I preferred it in wafer slim slices such as Prudencia had served. Large loaves of rustic bread and goat's cheese completed the meal. On the patio, Pitirri was entertaining the rest of the travellers with a mournful song – a Rondeña – telling of a bandit betrayed by his girlfriend and finally meeting a gruesome death at the hands of the *Guardia Civil*. He was probably still recovering from the earlier visit of the universally disliked police.

After an uneasy night on our lumpy, crackly mattresses, we rose early to the sound of church bells. Breakfast consisted of *churros*, fried by the street vendor in the square, dipped in thick, hot, sticky chocolate. The taste of goats' milk even pervaded the chocolate, but we were becoming accustomed to the strong animal flavour.

CHAPTER TWENTY

Almargen and the Legend of El Cid

"*A Spanish* posada *is a great leveller. Nobles and common people, masters and servants, horses and riders, mules, donkeys and pigs all share the same space.*" – Ian Robertson

News had arrived from Álora. Laura had received a telegram that her mother was ill and she was needed at home in California. She had already left.

"Poor Laura, what a blow for her." I did my best to hide my delight.

Susan was more direct.

She grinned, "that sort of leaves the playing field open."

I hugged myself. David was unmarried, and despite Antonio's warning about a number of girlfriends, he was mine to pursue for the next few days. With Laura hopefully out of the picture for good, I could be more direct.

We repacked our saddlebags and the grooms loaded up our patient steeds. John's sheepskin saddle cover had dried overnight and his ride promised to be more comfortable.

The usual group of pestering children, who were enjoying three months of freedom for the summer holidays, accompanied us as we left Campillos for our next stop, the village of Almargen. We were following what Antonio told us was a *camino real*, or royal road, used by the mule trains to cross the country.

A few miles from Campillos, we encountered a train of donkeys laden with wooden barrels in their rush panniers. They had journeyed from the coast and were carrying sardines and anchovies in salt to one of the inland towns. On their return journey, with the panniers empty, the muleteers would buy tomatoes and grapes to sell on the coast.

"*Con dios*," – go with God, they greeted David, who rode at the head of our small cavalcade.

Teams of large brown and white oxen ploughed the fields where, until recently, the corn had stood. As we passed under the fig trees, I reached up and picked some of the ripe purple fruit.

"Here, Susan, take one."

"Yuck." Susan had picked a fig full of ants. "They taste revolting. I know they eat ants in some countries but they are horribly bitter."

The striking hoopoes were all around us, unmistakable with their black and white wings, salmon pink bodies and black-tinged crests that rise when they are frightened or excited. The brilliant turquoise bee-eaters swooped and the air was filled with their raucous calls.

At several crossroads we had come upon wooden crosses.

"Who are they for?" asked Andrew.

Antonio replied, "Not so many years ago an unfortunate traveller met his death at the hands of some robbers on this road."

At last we were in bandit territory.

***

Almargen was one of the few villages we visited that did not sit on the mountainside, protected by a castle. This village was unassuming, with few airs and graces.

There were two *posadas*, and we were to stay in the one that was a former convent. Tucked into the corner of the shady square at the end of the Calle Correderas the *posada* was one of the oldest and 'quaintest' we had stayed in. The accommodation for the horses and mules was, as usual, excellent and, as usual, the travellers did not fare so well. The sleeping arrangements were so basic that there were no beds. No charge was made for the mattress on the floor allocated to each of us. Once again, Susan and I shared our small room with sacks of potatoes, garlic and all manner of farm implements.

"I wonder," she said "if we will ever get rid of the smell of garlic from our hair?"

It was so rudimentary that the charge was calculated per animal. As usual, there was no running water, but a constant stream of buckets from the well provided water for the horses and later enabled us to remove some of the dust of the day's ride. The *posada* was run by José, an ancient widower, assisted by Maria, his very short-tempered sister. Leaving Susan to get washed in our small room, I found David, alone for once, sitting outside a bar in the cobbled street.

"Come and join me. What do you want to drink?" I lowered myself into a chair beside him.

"What I really need is a very large glass of cold white wine."

"Coming up."

He returned with my drink and a *tapa* of fried blood sausage.

"So, how's it going? I mean the trip and Krishna. Are you getting along?"

"He's a great horse. I feel really safe with him." I licked my fingers after dealing with my rather greasy *tapa*.

"Shame about Laura." I remarked casually, sipping my wine.

"Yes, bad luck for her." David shrugged. "Anyway she wasn't going to do the ride. She only arrived in Álora the day before you, to learn Spanish."

"Oh, I got the impression you two were an item."

"Absolutely not. She's not into horses so that's a turn off for me. She looked like pretty hard work too."

I lounged back in my chair, digested this piece of good news and tried to conceal my joy. I imagined myself and David riding through the mountains together – with or without a sunset, it didn't matter. I looked at his hands – strong and capable, with golden hairs and long artistic fingers – and resisted the urge to touch them. I never anticipated falling in love in Andalucía, but was this warm feeling love?

David interrupted my reverie, "What about you, do you have a partner or a secret lover?"

"Neither. I left all that behind in England. This holiday is to be my great adventure, my search for romance, my dash for freedom."

"Freedom from what?"

"Oh, I don't know, just routine, boredom, boring men. I don't want to waste my life." I fished a fly out of my wine, "Spain is so wild, so romantic so stunningly over the top. There's just no comparison with Notting Hill."

"And what about these boring men?" he asked quizzically. "Do I fit into that description?"

I blushed.

"No, of course not. You seem to fit into the romantic category."

"I'm honoured. I'll try to live up to that."

Laughing he took my hand. "This hand is definitely not high maintenance, it's distinctly grubby. Oh shit, look out, here comes John. I'm not buying him a drink."

I arranged my face into a welcoming smile, whilst harbouring murderous thoughts.

"This place is a real tip," came the expected grouse from John.

"That's strange, Jill and I were just saying how romantic it was. Let's go and eat, Antonio will be waiting."

David took my arm and we joined the others. Susan raised her eyebrows but said nothing. I knew that I would have to explain later.

***

Later, as night fell, we sat over the remnants of a garlicky chicken. David and I were squashed together on one side of the table, legs touching unavoidably.

He nudged me. "You were talking of romance. Well, Antonio is the best storyteller ever of the romance of El Cid. Perhaps he will tell us."

"Antonio, do you know the real story? We've all seen the film with Charlton Heston and Sophia Loren but what is the Spanish version of the story?"

"*Bueno*," Antonio laughed. "It's a long story and a lot of it is legend and hearsay. Who knows what is really the true story."

"That's OK," Susan settled herself more comfortably, and poured more wine for us all. "You have just been nominated storyteller-in-chief for the rest of the ride. We've got nothing else to do."

"Well, once upon a time, there was a Spanish nobleman known as El Cid, whose real name was Rodrigo Díaz de Bivar. He fought for his king in numerous battles against the Moors. But when the one of King Fernando's warring sons, Alfonso, exiled him for a misdemeanour, he joined the Moors in the fight against his former sovereign. Sometimes he is unkindly described as an adventurer, a soldier of fortune, a hardened mercenary, ready to fight for anyone, Moor or Christian, who would pay him and his army. But he was not the only one who switched allegiances – the Christians fought amongst themselves, as did the various groups of Moors. Sometimes Christians fought alongside Moorish friends, or the roles were reversed.

The Moors named him El Cid, which means chief or lord, whilst the Spaniards called him El Campeador, champion.

He became such a famous warrior that Alfonso summoned him back from exile to fight at his side again. His horse, Babieca, was equally famous. When he was a young man, Rodrigo's godfather, a Carthusian monk in Burgos, offered to give him a horse from the herd of magnificent Andalucían horses bred by the monks. When Rodrigo chose Babieca, his godfather exclaimed "*Babieca, babieca*" – meaning idiot, as the horse was skinny and wild. Thus this great white warhorse, the most famous in Spanish history, was named "My idiot". The partnership in battle of horse and man became a legend. So precious was he to El Cid that he slept in the same room as his master."

Antonio paused in his narrative as Francisco, the bar owner, offered us a drink on the house. The four men settled for a glass of Spanish Fundador brandy.

"I'd rather have red wine," Susan decided.

"Yes, me too, that brandy's a killer."

When we were all served, Antonio resumed the story.

"An ancient Spanish ballad tells how El Cid's elderly father, Diego, was insulted and struck by a neighbour, Count Don Gomez. Too old and infirm to seek revenge, it fell to his two older sons to confront the count. However, the boys had no desire for bloodshed. Unable to forget the insult, elderly Diego lost his appetite, refused to leave the house, and could not sleep. Concerned to see how depressed and shamed his father was, El Cid sought out the aggressor and killed him. He returned home, and, calling his father, pointed to the count's head hanging from Babieca's saddle, still dripping blood. 'This will restore your appetite,' he told his father, who embraced him, declared him to be the new head of the household, and placed him at the head of the table.

"The dead count had a beautiful daughter, Jimena, who, far from being angry at her father's death, was dazzled by El Cid's reputation and reported good looks. It is said that once a woman has made up her mind there is no changing it, and Jimena resolved to have her knight in shining armour. Determined to marry him, she sought the help of King Fernando, who was in Burgos, and told him:

> I know he's born for thriving, none like him in the land
> I know that none in battle against his spear may stand,
> Forgiveness is well pleasing in God our Saviour's view
> And I forgive him freely for that my sire he slew.

The King summoned El Cid, who, mounted on Babieca, and accompanied by a personal army of three hundred men all dressed in matching cloaks, entered Burgos. Agreeing to the King's request that he should marry Jimena, the Cid proclaimed, 'Fair lady, by God's grace, an honoured husband thou shalt have, in thy dead father's place.'

"It seems they lived happily ever after until El Cid was killed in Valencia. Jimena brought up their children and put up with his continual absences in battle. The chroniclers tell us that he was faithful to his wife, even in the face of temptation.

"After a battle in which El Cid was the victor, he sent word to his commanders that the Moors should be allowed time to bury their dead. Touched by his clemency, the Moorish chieftain sent two of his most beautiful slave girls for El Cid's enjoyment. However, to the

Moor's surprise, they were returned with a message of 'Thanks, but no thanks – my wife Jimena is the only woman I want.'

"After the battle of Alcocer, in which his army overcame the Moors, weary from years of fighting and killing, he spared the life of the *caliph* of Zaragoza, al-Mutamin. The two men became great friends – the Moor was a great scholar, educated in mathematics and astrology at the University of Córdoba. He swore never to raise his sword again against the man he named El Cid and they fought alongside each other against the other Moorish armies in the battle of Valencia.

"The ballad of El Cid relates that one night in the year 1099 he had a vision. An old man with white hair appeared in the midst of a great light and surrounded by a sweet smell. He carried a bunch of keys. 'I am St Peter,' he told El Cid, 'Prince of the Apostles, and I come to warn you that you will die in thirty days. However, you will conquer the Moors, even after your death.' It is not clear whether El Cid then fell ill of a fever, or was gravely wounded in a skirmish near Valencia (it depends on the version of the ballad you believe), but he did die within the allotted thirty days. In the last seven days of his life he drank only rosewater, myrrh and a balsam sent to him by the Sultan of Persia. The weaker he became the stronger his voice, and 'his countenance grew fairer and fresher'. He instructed Jimena to have his body embalmed and mounted on his horse, upon his death. In his last hours he called for Babieca to be brought to him and legend says that the great horse cried tears on seeing his master for the last time.

"The body of the warrior was anointed with myrrh and balsam. With his famous sword Tizona (meaning 'terror of the world') in his hand, dressed in his coat of mail and mounted on Babieca, he rode out of Valencia accompanied by one thousand knights. At daybreak they reached the camp of the Moorish king. Terrified by the great number of white-robed knights led at full speed by the great warrior they had thought dead, mounted on Babieca, the Moorish king and all his army ran to the sea and swam to their ships. Twenty thousand Moors died that day. In death El Cid had saved Spain from the Moors, as he had so many times during his life.

"His wife refused to allow his 'fair and comely body' to be buried and he was placed in an ivory chair in the monastery of San Pedro de Cárdenas in Valencia, with his sword in his left hand, the strings of his cloak in his right. After his death, once a year his servant Gil Diaz and the abbot of the cathedral would distribute food and clothing to the poor in his memory. On the seventh anniversary, so many people had congregated for the ceremony that the abbot preached in the square outside the cathedral. The only person left inside was a Jew who had wandered into the church. As he stood before the body a thought occurred to him: 'This is the body of El Cid of whom they say no man ever touched his beard while he lived. I will touch his beard now and see what he can do to me.' He reached out to take hold of the beard, which while he lived was always protected by a net so no man should touch it. But God could not permit this, and he sent his spirit into the body of El Cid who released the strings of the cloak and withdrew his sword from its scabbard. The terrified Jew fell to the ground screaming. The abbot, hearing the commotion, found the Jew unconscious on the ground beside El Cid's chair. He called for holy water and threw it in the face of the prostrate man, demanding an explanation. The Jew told his story and begged to be baptised a Christian. The abbot named him Diego Gil. He lived for the rest of life in a monastery and cared for the embalmed body of El Cid, which remained in the cathedral for ten years. Jimena spent all her time at his side until her death. El Cid's faithful servant, Gil Diaz, cared for Babieca, but the great horse was never ridden again, and died two years after his beloved master, at the age of forty. His last instructions to the groom were, 'When you bury Babieca, dig deep, for shameful thing it were that he should be eaten by curs, who has trampled down so much currish flesh of Moors'.

"On his deathbed El Cid asked that Jimena and Babieca be buried next to him. All three were finally laid to rest in the Cathedral in Burgos after the War of Independence in the early 1900s. However, during that war the grave was looted and El Cid's bones were stolen by a French officer, General Thiébault (according to the writer and traveller Théophile Gautier), who kept them in his bed, touching them every morning in the hope that some of El Cid's bravery would rub off on him."

Antonio picked up his glass.

"And that is the tale of El Cid."

We all toasted his storytelling.

"Yes," observed David, "that's what it is, just a tale with many versions, handed down through generations."

"But it's so romantic," breathed Susan. "I cried buckets in the movie when Charlton Heston rode out on Babieca along the beach to do battle. I've never heard of another horse named Babieca. You'll have to name your next one after that great warhorse, Antonio."

"It's a beautiful tale," I agreed. "I remember Louisa Tenison wrote, 'Spain has ever been the favoured land of romance, a land of bygone chivalry.'"

"I read recently that El Cid's heirs are not so chivalrous and are still fighting over ownership of his sword, Tizona," said Andrew. "Apparently there were rumours that it was a fake but after analysis of some of the metal it was confirmed that it was made round the year 1040. It looks as if the Tizona in the museum in Burgos is the real thing. It must be worth a lot of money."

He stretched. "It's late, and I'm for bed."

"Me too," said Susan.

There was clearly no possibility of continuing my conversation with David as he had moved over the other side of the table and he and Antonio seemed to have settled down for a nightcap, so I also decided to catch up on some sleep. We paused to pick the scented jasmine flowers, which in theory deter the mosquitoes, and passed through the stables where our horses were resting.

Pitirri, stretched out on the hay with his head on a saddle, was snoring loudly.

CHAPTER TWENTY-ONE

Shopping

In the morning we were awoken by the raucous chant of the rag and bone man under our window.

"I fix saucepans and all types of china – I sell ceramic bowls, small, medium and large – all cheap. I buy old iron, old beds, metal and copper…"

His cart was laden with a variety of lumps of metal and was pulled by a lugubrious chestnut mule who stood chewing on the prickly branches of the orange tree beside the *posada* gate in a desultory manner.

Breakfast consisted of *migas con chocolate*. This strange mixture consists of breadcrumbs steeped in water, sprinkled with salt, hot oil, and garlic. Eggs fried in olive oil top the dish and a cup of hot thick chocolate completes the meal. The combination of tastes was interesting to say the least.

Antonio had announced a later start. Susan and I needed to buy shampoo to attempt to eliminate the aroma of garlic, so we strolled out in search of the only shop in Almargen, Ultramarinos Encarni. After enquiring of several women armed with shopping baskets, we found the shop. *Ultramarinos* literally means from over the sea, and in this tiny little shop she did indeed stock some exotic articles. Among the usual packs of washing soap and biscuits were to be found cloves, ginger, cinnamon, pepper, coffee, and tea, which were still luxuries beyond the reach of most pockets in the village. Saucepans, frying pans, earthenware drinking pots, plaits of raffia, and sacks of chickpeas scrambled for space with home-made sausages, lumps of rancid pork fat and bones for the stew pot. In a corner behind the counter a toothless black-clad old man sat on a rush chair, sucking noisily at biscuits which he had dunked in a glass of milk.

"*Buenos días,*" we greeted the two women already being served. A sudden silence fell on what, before our arrival, had been an animated conversation. The old man continued to suck on his biscuits, belching occasionally, whilst the women silently inspected our attire from head to foot. Encarni pulled herself together, and attempted a smile. A customer was a customer, even if she wore trousers.

"What do you want."

"We want shampoo please."

She disappeared to the back of the shop. In an instant the shop filled with local women anxious to catch a glimpse of these strange women who rode horses like men and slept in *posadas* like muleteers.

"*Serán suecas,*" they must be Swedish, I heard a large multi-coloured lady announce knowledgeably, as if we were deaf as well as immoral.

"My son has seen Swedish girls in Torremolinos and he says they wear trousers. These must be Swedish."

"You don't say," puffed her friend in the purple smock with psychedelic yellow sunflowers straining over her ample bosom.

"They wear bikinis on the beach," Multi-coloured added, fanning herself in outrage at the thought of such scandalous behaviour and the outsize lady in the psychedelic sunflowers repeated:

"Bikinis. Shameful, if you ask me."

How shameful indeed: almost naked in bikinis when on the beach, and in trousers when elsewhere. It was too much for the god-fearing ladies to bear. Encarni returned with the shampoo and we dug in our pockets for loose change.

"Do you think we should pretend to speak Swedish?" grinned Susan.

The old man belched loudly again and I didn't dare look at Susan in case I started to laugh.

"Where are their husbands, I'd like to know," said a woman in blue, the same shape as the other two, folding her arms righteously over her tightly corseted stomach, her moustache bristling.

"Mercedes in the *posada* says they're not married to the men they're with."

"Just as well my Paco is out in the fields today. I wouldn't want him seeing these women."

"Yes, my Juan has taken the mule to market, thank goodness."

Double chins wobbling threateningly, she turned her back on us. There was a general murmur of disapproval from the worthy matrons and I pushed Susan towards the door.

"*Adios señoras,*" I called, as we ran the gauntlet of outraged heaving bosoms.

"We'd better go before they lynch us as foreign harpies. Imagine *them* in bikinis."

Giggling helplessly we beat a retreat with our shampoo, and had to sit down on the edge of the fountain to control our mirth, to the surprise of two elderly men already occupying the space. Perhaps fearing the wrath of their wives if they were caught near such wicked women, they grabbed their straw hats and walking sticks and hobbled off as fast as their elderly legs would take them. At least in the bar they would be safe. Women were not allowed into village bars and a small medicinal snifter of brandy would steady their nerves.

"You two may laugh!" David had come in search of us. "But a girl I know had stones thrown at her in Ronda for walking in the street in trousers."

Spain was definitely different.

My heart was jumping uncontrollably at the sight of him.

"Come on, the horses are ready and we're leaving for Teba."

CHAPTER TWENTY-TWO

Teba and Robert the Bruce

"Those say that set eyes on him
when happy, loveable was he
and meek and sweet in company.
But those with him in battle saw
another countenance he wore!"
– John Barbour, *The Brus* (*The Bruce*)

We reached the village of Teba in the late afternoon. From many kilometres distant we had been able to see the Castle of the Star, silhouetted against the blue Ronda mountains. Clinging to the mountainside, high on a rocky saddle, it was a perfect situation for a fortress and it was here that I was to discover a legend of my forebears in the narrow cobbled streets. I had come to Andalucía to follow in the steps of great travellers and, to my surprise, found one of my ancestors. My family can trace our ancestry back to Robert the Bruce, but I had no idea of the connection with this tiny village in the mountains of Andalucía.

In the tiny museum in the centre of the village, decorated with Roman and Moorish pottery, the story of Teba's link to Scotland was chronicled in ancient books guarded in glass cabinets. History relates that in 1329, when King Robert knew he was dying from leprosy he called the nobles of his Scottish kingdom to Cardross Castle. He had intended to visit the Holy Land to fight against the Moors, the enemies of Christ, but due to his failing health he asked his nobles to carry his heart into battle. Sir James Douglas (Black Douglas), one of the King's bravest knights, volunteered, and when the king died some three months later, aged only 54, his heart was placed in a silver and enamel locket, which Douglas placed round his neck.

Accompanied by a group of knights and gentlemen, Douglas's party left for Europe. It is not clear why he travelled via Seville in Andalucía, but it is known to have been an alternative route to the Holy Land. When Douglas arrived in Seville he was received by King Alfonso XI. The battles against the Moors in Spain were ongoing and in 1330 they threatened the villages of Ardales and Teba.

There wasn't too much going on in the Holy Land so Douglas and King Alfonso decided to join in battle against the infidels outside Teba. During the skirmish James Douglas was confused by a trumpet signal and believed he had been given the order to attack, but it led him into an ambush from which they had to fight hard to escape. Douglas turned and saw that one of his knights, William Sinclair of Roslyn, had been cut off and was in great danger. With ten of his men he turned to assist him, crying, "Alas yonder worthy knight shall perish but for present help." He threw the locket containing his king's heart amongst the Moors, shouting, "Go as you desired, and I will follow you or die."

He was killed, history tells us, because he was not wearing the customary uniform of the crusaders, which would have been respected by the Moors. He bore on his sleeve his own arms, consisting of three stars on a blue background, which they did not recognize. His surviving men could not leave his body on foreign soil so he was boiled in vinegar until his flesh fell off the bones. The flesh was buried in Spain and his bones were returned to Scotland and are to be found in the Kirk of Douglas. Robert the Bruce's heart is buried in Melrose Abbey. The arms of the Douglas clan still bear a red heart below the three stars in memory of their king.

As the curator of the museum proudly showed us some remnants of the battle flags, he told us that in the village of Teba today, when the children misbehave, they are still threatened with the ghost of Black Douglas.

CHAPTER TWENTY-THREE

We ride to Arriate

The *posada* in Teba was spotlessly clean and the beds surprisingly comfortable. Or perhaps we were just becoming accustomed to the lumpy mattresses. After an uneventful night and a late breakfast, midday found us riding west towards the village of Arriate, crossing the railway line that led to Granada.

"So, have you found any bandits yet?" David teased.

"Don't be facetious. I know there aren't any but I love just travelling the roads they used and using the *posadas* where they slept. It's incredible – it's almost as if time has stood still and nothing has changed."

"Yes, the *posada* patios with the mules and their bells have real atmosphere. You can almost see the bandits riding in at night, and the colours in the muleteers' gear just beg to be painted. I've done some sketches, but the riders haven't come out too well. I'm better at drawing animals than people."

Krishna suddenly leapt off the ground with all four feet as a covey of partridges took flight from under his feet.

"Hey there, chico, it's all right," David calmed him and took his bridle, as I rearranged saddlebags and retrieved my stirrups. "So what are you going to do when this holiday is over? Are you going back to England?"

"I want to see a bit more of Spain before I leave, but it depends on money – I'm really short, so I can't stay too long. But if nothing else I want to go to Granada."

Just as I had at last managed a few minutes' uninterrupted conversation with David, John's whining tone came from behind us.

"David, how much longer before we arrive?"

"Only about another hour. What's the matter?"

"It's just too hot today. Why can't we travel later in the evening?"

Patiently David pulled his horse back alongside John.

"Just think of that ice-cold beer. It'll be worth waiting for."

The *posada* was situated at the junction of four streets in the centre of the village. To our amazement and joy there was the great luxury of a bathroom with running water and a bathtub.

"Don't waste the water," Ana, the owner of the *posada*, scolded us. "There's enough in there for four people."

Susan and I tossed a coin for first turn in the clean water. Although lethargic, the flow from the taps was a welcome relief from the clumsy ablutions in a bucket or bowl. The water was icy cold, which discouraged us from spending too much time in the bath, but I was glad to be reminded of how it felt to have clean hair.

After our wash, we found Antonio in the stables chatting with two men who appeared to be gypsy horse dealers. They were checking out the horses' teeth and nodding approvingly at their condition.

"But they're too fat, Antonio," opined the older of the two gypsies, a tall, almost black-skinned man whose mop of grey hair was at odds with his swarthy skin. "I'll offer you two of mine who are fitter and will last you longer," he said, as he puffed on his cigar.

"No way, Miguel," laughed Antonio. "I like my horses fat and happy and they work hard for their feed. Yours wouldn't last more than a week with the distances we travel."

Krishna put his ears back and made it obvious he was not impressed with the way the dealers were waving their sticks at him.

Andrew had entered the stable behind me.

"Have you seen the nails on those guys' little fingers? Look how long they are."

"They are revolting," whispered Susan. "Long and filthy. Do all gypsies have nails like that?"

"I don't think Pitirri has. At least I haven't noticed."

"I think I read somewhere that one long fingernail used to be a sign of wealth."

Antonio, Susan and I took a stroll round the village, and sat on the bridge over the stream watching the women washing clothes on the smooth stones of the river. Not for them the modern running water of the *posada*, but a long walk from their homes and back with heavy tin baths full of washing. During the day, the clothes would be spread out to dry on the river bank, with the oleanders and rushes being used as improvised washing lines.

"Look at that boy carrying those big water containers," Susan said, pointing to where a young man with beetling brows and haunting dark eyes was struggling up the steep cobbled streets to deliver the water to the houses at the top of the village. The water was carried in big glass jars with a protective covering of cane with handles. Each jar must have contained at least twenty litres of water.

"He's completely deaf so he can't talk either," Antonio waved at the boy. "He's got no family so far as I know, so he depends on this job to survive."

Searching for a bar to settle the dust of the day's ride we opted for a small café from which we could observe village life passing by. At a table outside the casino sat a number of gypsy horse traders, deep in conversation, filling the evening air with the aroma of contraband cigars. Casinos are the Spanish equivalent of men's clubs. Women are strictly forbidden to enter and the club provides a haven from female nagging. Members gamble, meet friends and trade anything from contraband cigars to horses and olives. Negotiations between the gypsy traders would last late into the night before the horses changed hands.

Ever-curious about the civil war, although I knew it was a taboo subject, for the first time, I dared to raise it with Antonio. I had assumed he was right-wing and on Franco's side, but he had never revealed his political opinions.

"I know we really aren't supposed to mention it, but this village is so close to Ronda where the war was bad. What happened here – or can't you tell me?"

"Arriate was mainly a Republican village," Antonio told us quietly. "They suffered badly and most of the men were killed when they came out of hiding. The women turned to smuggling – they are so close to Gibraltar. But many were also caught and executed. You can see it is still a very poor village. The remaining men now work on the roads breaking stones, and the little boys are hired out to local landowners as shepherds. They start work when they are seven or eight and earn very little money. These small villages have found it very difficult to recover from the troubles. Interestingly, the people of Ronda have always looked down on the inhabitants of Arriate – they call them country bumpkins. Anyhow, it is time to get back, our dinner will be waiting for us." He had clearly said all he was prepared to on the matter.

Antonio had organized an early meal as we were all tired from the intense heat and the many hours we had spent in the saddle in the past few days.

"Tomorrow will be easier," he reassured us. "Ronda is only a few hours' ride away."

Dinner at the *posada* was served in a little private dining room and consisted of *salmorejo* – a type of solid *gazpacho* – and horror of horrors, pigs' tripe in tomato sauce with chickpeas. I manoeuvred the chickpeas away from the tripe and, catching Susan's eye, passed the offending glutinous pieces on to her plate.

"For goodness sake, help me out with these fatty bits."

Susan chewed with relish.

"At least it's not cat, it's not bony enough. Pretend it's chicken, then it's not so bad. And anyway, I'm starving."

CHAPTER
TWENTY-FOUR

The Romance of Ronda

"I cross your border, hail and peace in God, sundered rocks. Hail and peace, crags, mountains, scrub, woods, currents; health, peace and happiness, nobility, friends, blood – my land." – Vicente Espinel

Set high up on its rocky pinnacle and surrounded by mountain ranges, Ronda is visible from many kilometres away. Under a diaphanous sky, I was at last travelling on the route the English travellers took from Gibraltar. Almost without exception they raved about its charms. The romantics wrote glowingly of "a poetic and inaccessible Moorish town", "the dream of my old age", and the "mysterious soul of Ronda". Albert Calvert, a French traveller called it "the romantic capital of a romantic region".

However, after a difficult and uncomfortable journey through the mountains, George Cayley wrote of his disappointment with "a straggling unremarkable town which might have been a suburb of Bradford."

The town has been called the "eagle's nest" partly because of the situation high in the mountains where the golden eagle rules, but also because the bravery of the inhabitants is likened to that of eagles.

Perched astride a deep dark ravine, *El Tajo*, through which runs the River Guadalvin, the town has retained many of its

Arab characteristics. Streets still bear their Moorish names and the mezquita is well preserved. In the depth of the ravine are the remains of Moorish mills. In Moorish times it is said that the town was surrounded by forests full of wild animals. The El Tajo gorge is spanned by two bridges, the Roman one and the New Bridge, completed in 1793.

As we approached along the valley, marvelling at this fortress town before us, I almost expected to see smugglers and highwaymen riding before us, as in the Doré illustrations. Donkeys laden with earthenware pots and mules with bales of cloth struggled up the old Roman track, entering the town by the arch as they had from time immemorial.

Since Ronda is a big town, the *posada* was large, with an impressive arched entrance. However, there were no rooms available, so whilst the horses and the grooms remained there, we were to sleep in the *fonda*, in the main street. By custom *posadas* are only obliged to offer lodging, salt and cooking facilities, whereas the *fonda* offers the traveller food and drink. To our joy there was running water in the basins and a proper toilet. Situated in the centre, it was ideally placed to explore the town on foot. The horses and Pitirri and Sebastian could enjoy a well-earned rest.

A large number of mules and donkeys, all travelling south with cargoes of fruit, were already tethered in the spacious stables at the *posada* and a strong smell of garlic and onions pervaded the central patio where several muleteers were preparing their daily meal over a fire. The level of noise was deafening, and I was glad we would not be sleeping here.

Many, indeed most, of the nineteenth century travellers complained bitterly about the *posadas*. The lack of plumbing, no glass in the windows, excess wildlife amongst the wool of the mattresses, the smells of fried oil and garlic spreading into every nook and cranny. Nor did the female *posada* owners escape their criticism. Gautier was greeted by a "wrinkle-visaged old harridan, who oiled her features into a species of a smile."

D'Avillier's hostess was:

An old wrinkled crone, whose nose and chin were cultivating a growing attachment to each other, whose great age it was impossible to determine. She was stooping over half a dozen mysterious earthen pots that were simmering on the fire, emitting a foul odour of rancid oil.

The beds were comfortable compared with the *posadas* we had become used to, and the owners didn't seem to be more ugly than usual. But there was one thing that clearly hadn't changed since the nineteenth century – the mosquitoes. They fell upon our Anglo-Saxon blood like rapacious vampires. Dundas Murray declared that a notice should be posted at the door of any Andalucían hostelry: "Here you may spend a night entertaining the carnivorous inhabitants of your bed. Rise early, happy to flee from the vampires who have invaded your bed."

Some travellers, he reported, slept in a type of large sleeping bag, whilst he put on long johns into which his feet were tucked and was tied at the waist with a tight cord. Cotton gloves, a night cap and a scarf to protect the neck were also useful protection.

CHAPTER TWENTY-FIVE

The Town of Ronda

"In Ronda men of eighty are only children."
– Traditional saying

After a comfortable night in the *fonda* we rose early to explore Ronda. Fortified by a dubious breakfast, we set forth, cameras at the ready.

"I think the *posada* would have been better than this *fonda*," grumbled John. "The kitchen was revolting."

But the town awaited us, and rancid butter and dirty kitchens were unimportant on that crisp and beautiful morning.

David was our guide as we dropped down the steep road to the centre of the town and the bullring, he seemed pleased for an opportunity to show off his knowledge of his passion for fighting bulls.

"The ring is one of the oldest in Spain, and is known as the cradle of bullfighting. In truth, bullfighting dates from the time of the Moorish occupation and was not considered a sport, but preparation for war and a method of keeping the horses fit. In times of peace, the rival Moslem and Christian knights engaged in friendly competitions," David explained on the way. "It's one of the few bullrings that has covered seats for protection from the rain and the sun."

Seated in cool doorways around the bullring, the harness-makers stitched head collars made from bullrushes with bells, while a muleteer waited patiently for his boots to be repaired.

We entered through the patio where the bullfighters and horses gather before a fight, and met our guide, Francisco. He was a dark-skinned, wizened little man of indeterminate age, with very bandy legs and a pronounced limp.

"Francisco was a bullfighter," David told us, "but he was gored really badly. It happened in a small bullring near Sevilla and there was no doctor available. He's lucky to be alive. Now he makes a living showing tourists round."

It didn't seem the right moment to ask, as an animal lover, how often the bull won the fight. But Francisco had obviously come a bad second in his encounter with 500 kilos of angry bull.

He told us that the Real Maestranza de Caballeria de Ronda was founded in 1572 by King Philip II for training in all forms of horsemanship. The riders became expert in training their horses to avoid the sharp horns of the bulls. Queen Isabella attempted to pass an edict ordering the bulls' horns to be covered to avoid maiming the horses or the bullfighters. However it was deemed unfair on the bull to remove his chance of revenge on his tormentors and the edict never took effect.

In the eighteenth century, bullfighting on foot was introduced, and the most famous matador of that era was Pedro Romero. Born into a family of bullfighters, his courage and artistic prowess was legendary. His success as a lover was evident from his affairs with both the Duchess of Alba and the Queen of Spain. But, in line with the double standards of the time, in a fit of jealousy he threw his wife into the *Tajo* after finding her in bed with a rival. Every year a bullfight in costumes of the era of Goya is held to remember his birthday.

The Ordóñez family of bullfighters rose to fame, particularly Cayetano and his son Antonio. Orson Welles and Ernest Hemingway were fascinated by the bullfight and followed the progress of the Ordóñez family. Hemingway wrote of the rivalry between the famous matadors Antonio Ordóñez and his brother-in-law, José

Luis Dominguín, in his novel, *The Dangerous Summer*. He followed them throughout Spain during the bullfighting season and his book was published after his suicide. Today, there are streets in Ronda named after both Hemingway and Welles.

Francisco talked us through the intricacies of a bullfight. None of us had seen one and, as animal lovers, we all had very mixed feelings.

"The bullfighters parade into the ring through this door," he told us. "They are accompanied by all their assistants – *banderilleros*, who place the darts in the back of the bull's neck, and the *picadors* on their horses. They have long poles with a metal spike which helps to lower the bull's head. This may seem cruel, but helps the *matador* to kill the bull quickly. The horses wear padding to protect them.

"Do they get hurt?" Susan wanted to know.

"The horses? Not often. Only if the horse is knocked over by the bull and his padding is torn."

At the beginning of the fight the matador is in the ring alone with the bull and uses his *capote* – the big pink and ochre cape. He uses this time to judge which horn the bull will hook with and sometimes to find out if the bull has good eyesight. Some matadors do a pass on their knees when the bull first comes out, but this is very dangerous. Then the *banderilleros* place the sticks decorated with coloured paper which have a small arrow head on the end. These men need to be very agile as they have to go in over the bull's head.

The *picadors* on their horses come next, and the crowd always boos as they don't want the picador to weaken the bull and spoil the fight. Sometimes a bull won't leave the horse alone and the picador is obliged to keep protecting the horse by wounding the bull with his lance more than he should. This will tire the bull and make for a more boring fight. Finally the *matador* takes his sword and his red cape, his *muleta*, and plays the bull. Like this." Francisco struck a pose with an imaginary cape and bull. "Hey *toro*." As the make-believe bull rushed past him he waved to an imaginary crowd and bowed. He grinned, "If the bull is brave and noble the *matador* will fight it for about five minutes. If it is dangerous or not to his liking he will try and kill it as soon as possible and go home safely. The death of the bull is the moment of truth."

He showed us the small museum with bullfighters suits, stuffed bulls heads, a collection of some gruesome swords and the collection of ornately embroidered capes worn by *matadors* as they enter the ring.

As we stood close together in the small, poorly lit room, our fingers touched and I felt David's lips brush the back of my neck. The lingering caress was so unexpected it left me breathless. "Don't stop," I whispered.

"Let's have a drink alone later," he breathed in my ear. "After dinner."

"What are you two whispering about?" Susan broke the spell.

"Nothing in particular. Come on, Francisco is waiting." Reluctantly I moved down the narrow passageway that led to the main bullring, where two young bullfighters, *novilleros*, had just entered the ring to practise their passes. We watched, fascinated, as one with a cape and mock sword, challenged 'the bull' – a pair of horns mounted on a bicycle, pushed by his friend. Repeatedly the 'bull' charged, in slow motion, snorting ferociously and realistically, giving the apprentice a chance to perfect his stance and timing, watched and corrected by an older man standing in the shadows behind the *burladero*, a wooden barrier surrounding the ring.

"What a stroke of luck," David said enthusiastically, looking over at the figure leaning over the barrier. "That man over there is the famous bullfighter Antonio Ordóñez himself. He lives in Ronda and he probably sponsors one of the young bullfighters. Let's find out. But keep quiet and don't disturb their concentration."

We moved quietly round the narrow passageway. A small group of men leaned over the barrier, intent on the progress of the two young bullfighters. It was clear that Antonio was very much in charge and the rest of the group deferred to him. I had imagined all bullfighters to be dark gypsy-like men – thin and wiry, like Francisco. But Antonio was tall, with dark hair slicked back. He was broad shouldered and his body was well muscled – probably about ten years older than me.

"Keep your feet still, Jose," instructed Antonio. "The bull must come to you. Wait till he charges. Now straighten that arm." He sighed with frustration. "God give me patience, he's so wooden, he's like a puppet, he needs to train more. Take over Rafael please. I despair of him."

"He's very good-looking," whispered Susan. She rummaged in her bag for her camera. "Do you think he'll mind if I take his photo, David?"

"Best ask him first."

"*Hola maestro Antonio,*" David shook the great man's hand. "May I introduce these friends who are travelling with me and Antonio Llomelini from Álora on horseback? Are these some of your protégés?"

Antonio nodded.

"José is supposed to be under my wing but I have little patience when they don't train. They should live, eat and breathe bullfighting. But today's youth, all they seem to think about is women. At their age I was running up and down mountains to get fit," he laughed. "I have little patience as a teacher. So David, how is my good friend el Marqués Antonio Llomelini?"

"He's fine. I think he is checking the blacksmith's work on the horses."

"That was a terrible thing to happen to his girl friend – what was her name? – Vicki, I think."

"Yes, it seemed so pointless. Such a waste." David frowned at me – rightly anticipating my curiosity.

"And you *señoritas*, are you *aficionadas* of bullfighting?"

"None of us have ever seen one and I think we're all animal lovers," Susan skilfully fielded that awkward question.

"I worry about the horses. I would hate to see one hurt or killed. I know it's hypocritical but I don't worry so much about the bull," I added.

Antonio looked at me with amusement.

"And what about the man. Do you not worry about him getting hurt?"

"That never happens. It's cruel, it's a one-way fight," John interrupted from the back.

David frowned at his rudeness, but Antonio ignored him and looked at me.

"Well, I don't know where your route will take you but I am due to fight in the annual fair at La Linea near Gibraltar in two weeks' time. If you are in the area come and see me at the hotel and I'll give you tickets. If I do my best to make sure neither the horse nor I get hurt, will you come?"

"That would be fantastic. If I can be there I will. David has told us all about your rivalry with your brother-in-law, Luis Dominguín. Will he fight in La Linea too?"

"No, I don't think we are billed together. But you never know. Now I must go and see how young José is doing." Raising his hand in a salute he turned back to watch his young apprentice. "Arm straight," he bellowed.

Andrew was watching the training session from a shady seat on the other side of the ring. David waved at him to join us and we left the relative cool of the bullring and emerged blinking into the searing heat.

"That was great to meet him. Andrew, did you hear, he invited us to a bullfight."

Andrew looked uncertain.

"Are you sure you want to go? I'm still in two minds about it."

"Yes, it's amazing. He promised the horse wouldn't get hurt."

David winked Andrew.

"I thought I was in with a chance but I think she just fell in love with a bullfighter."

"Well you have to admit he's romantic – not at all boring."

"Definitely a womanizer," opined Susan sagely, "I can tell.".

***

We walked down the main street towards the New Bridge and leaned over the wall looking down into the murky depths of the Tajo ravine. The huge boulders and the sound of the bounding river were breathtaking. To the left of the bridge is the "Moor's chair" which overlooks the gorge.

"Why is it called that, David?"

"They say that a young Christian captain and his beautiful Moorish girlfriend used to sit here, even though relationships between the two religions were forbidden. The father of the girl determined to stop the romance and attempted to have the young man arrested. As they fled from the pursuers, the couple embraced and they threw themselves to their death in the depths of the ravine. The distraught father sat on the Moor's seat every day until his own death."

Doré was so inspired by the ravine that he used it to illustrate his drawings of Dante's *Inferno*.

Until recently, animal corpses were thrown into the Tajo to feed the vultures and other scavengers living on the rocky precipices, and during the civil war, prisoners from both sides of the conflict were thrown to a terrifying death on to the boulders below.

"Look at that peregrine falcon," John said, leaning dangerously over the edge of the bridge, camera in hand.

"Take care, John, it's a long way down," warned David.

"Those falcons have only really got one predator – the eagle owl. His favourite foods are peregrine falcon chicks, rabbits, and sometimes small cats," David told me as we sat together on one of the stone benches and admired the view.

Aloes, prickly pears, and trailing rock plants, with their roots sprouting from the ancient walls, covered the sides of the ravine. Choughs planed through the narrow archway and an ancient fig tree with gnarled, wind-blown branches hung perilously onto a sheer rock face.

"Look down to the right," David said as he took my hand and pointed. "Past the distant mountains surrounding the city is the Sierra de San Cristóbal – a famous bandit stronghold. Although I'm not sure you would find any there now," he said with a smile.

I laughed. "Maybe I don't need a bandit now. Perhaps a knowledgeable guide or a handsome bullfighter can be just as romantic?"

"Well if you're looking for an expert guide, I had better see what else I can remember about this place."

"Down on the left you see the old Roman bridge, which used to be the only way of crossing to the old part of the town known as the *mercadillo* or little market. When the town authorities announced a heavy levy on all goods entering the town, in defiance the merchants set up a market outside the town walls to avoid the tax."

David explained that largely due to its situation on the main route through to central and north Spain, Ronda was of great importance. The Moorish influence was obvious everywhere, from the thirteenth century baths and remains of the gateway to the city, to the well preserved fourteenth century minaret. Greece, Carthage and Rome all left their stamp on the town, and the six centuries of Romanization and eight of Muslim occupation were not easily eradicated by future invaders.

King Fernando took Ronda from the Moors in 1485 when the Muslim governor, Hamet el Zegrí, had gone to the relief of the village of Coin, to the north of Málaga. A siege of Coin and neighbouring villages was planned to distract the Moors' attention from the real purpose, which was the taking of Ronda. Meantime, a Christian army would also attempt to conquer the city of Málaga. The siege of Ronda lasted just ten days, and King Fernando travelled in triumph on to Córdoba to meet his wife, the Queen Isabella. When Hamet el Zegrí returned his eagle's nest was in Christian hands. Enraged that he had been so duped, he returned to the siege of Málaga, where he was executed after the siege.

During the Napoleonic War (also known as the Peninsular War and the War of Independence), made famous in Britain by the novels and television series of *Sharpe* by Bernard Cornwell, Ronda fought bravely against the French invaders. Napoleon Bonaparte entered the city in 1810, with an army of ninety thousand men. He proclaimed "Spaniards, after a long agony your nation is perishing. I have seen your ills and I shall remedy them." As the French armies robbed, raped, and pillaged their way through Spain, humiliating the population, the hatred for the invaders and the desire for vengeance mounted. Guerrilla bands sprung from the undergrowth and harried and tormented the French troops. In the mountains of Ronda they were joined by bandits and smugglers who, at the outset of the war, had been wanted men. Now times had changed and they were invaluable to their country for their knowledge of the countryside and especially the best hiding places. Napoleon had misjudged the untrained guerrillas and ultimately this was to cost him dearly.

The French General published a decree in which he ordered his men to destroy all walls, hedges and fields alongside the roads so that no bandits could use them as cover for an attack on his troops. Any farmer found guilty of harbouring Spanish guerrillas would be arrested by the French army and his house would be destroyed.

The French atrocities continued, fuelling hatred and hardship. One hundred and fifty villagers were burned alive in the local church. Nuns were raped and hung from the trees round the convent. Spanish women found to be consorting with the French had their tongues and breasts cut off.

In one town, one hundred French soldiers were captured by guerrillas and buried with their heads above ground level. With cannon balls, the guerrillas played bowls with the heads until their necks were broken. Women also played their part in the guerrilla activities, using knives and scissors to kill and maim whenever they found a lone French soldier. Meanwhile, English troops under the command of Wellington and an untidy rabble of poorly paid and underfed Spanish troops were advancing through Spain, scattering the French before them. The English troops' appalling behaviour towards the local population in the towns of Badajoz and Salamanca where they inflicted unprecedented violence on the very people they had come to liberate, caused much concern in Britain, as the British had been so quick to criticize the atrocities committed by the French.

In Ronda there were, as in most conflicts, collaborators, who were known as *afrancesados*, literally French sympathisers. The majority of the collaborators were members of the Town Council, the intelligentsia, and rich landowners who believed that the French might bring stability to war-torn Spain and that coincidentally they might themselves profit from troubled waters.

The occupation of Ronda lasted just thirty months before the French were ousted by a combination of the English and Spanish troops and local guerrilla groups who shot and killed the French general Boussain. The fleeing troops destroyed all in their path. The *afrancesados*, whatever their motives for their collaboration, were summarily tried and thrown into the Tajo gorge. The war dragged on in the rest of Spain until 1813, when Wellington finally crossed the Pyrenees into France.

I was enthralled by the history of this rocky town, the gateway to the endless sierras and the villages and magic of Andalusia. Poetry and romance, but also so much bloodshed. Unquiet ghosts from many centuries must walk the ancient streets on dark nights.

CHAPTER
TWENTY-SIX

More of Ronda; the Tuna

*"Imagine a compact and walled town cloven in twain
by a fearful chasm nigh 300 feet deep, from the bottom
of which a foaming and boiling stream sends its roar
upwards."* – Dundas Murray

Although the air was crisp the heat became intense as midday
approached. Andrew and Susan declared that they had done enough
sightseeing for one day and returned to the cool of the fonda patio.
John and I followed David into the Church of Saint Mary, fragrant
from the myrtle hedges surrounding it. Set in a small square with
gardens reminiscent of the Alhambra in Granada, this was originally
a mosque; it had been converted into a church by King Fernando.
Whilst it suffered some damage in the civil war, most of the building
escaped the destruction meted out to many of the churches by
republicans. Ronda's sympathies lay squarely with the republican
side and when Franco's nationalists took over the town, many of the
prominent republican citizens were summarily executed.

We returned to the centre of the town via the Casa del Rey Moro,
the house of the Moorish king where the Prince Al-Mohamed
allegedly had the skulls of his enemies mounted in gold and used as
wine glasses. The house was never used as a residence by the Moorish
king, but its overriding importance for the city was as a water mine.

In the fourteenth century, under the rule of King Abomelik, Ronda was constantly in the firing line between the warring Moors and the Christians. During the frequent sieges water was essential to the survival of the inhabitants. Within the house is a staircase leading down to the River Guadalvín from whence water could be carried up in leather skins. It is said that innumerable Christian slaves died in the construction of the staircase.

David led us down part of the staircase. "We won't go all the way down, but come into this room they call the Secret Room. It has an incredibly strange feature. If two people stand at opposite ends of the room they can speak together and a person standing in the middle of the room can't hear anything they say. Here, Jill, you stand at one end and John stand at the other, and have a conversation. I'll stand in the middle and you'll see what I mean." He was right. "Curiouser and curiouser" as Alice in Wonderland said.

"I'm sure there is a scientific explanation but I've never heard it." David led the way out into the brilliant sunlight.

"Let's go and eat, I'm starving."

Lunch at the *fonda* consisted of *ajo blanco*, a thick chilled soup of almonds, garlic and saffron, garnished with. white grapes. The soup was followed by a bowl of tomatoes, thinly sliced onions and slices of fresh goats cheese.

"We should be losing weight with all the vegetables we're eating," said Susan, pulling her stomach in hopefully.

"It's too hot to eat," moaned John. "I never thought it would be this bad. I'm going to bed."

"God he's a pain, but he's right. I'm off for a siesta, coming?" Susan added.

"Good idea," I agreed.

As we climbed the stairs Susan casually asked, "Hey, I meant to ask you how are things going with David? I saw you two whispering together this morning."

"At the speed of an old mule, as somebody once said. It's hard to get time alone, but I'm working on it. At least Laura is out of the equation."

Susan frowned.

"You'd better hurry up. We're almost half way through the ride. I know I'm interfering, but if you fancy him, you'd better make a move."

I laughed.

"Listen to the expert. How long have you been engaged, and still can't make your mind up?"

Susan laughed and I threw myself on my bed.

"Don't worry, I've got the matter well in hand," I said with more confidence than I actually felt.

Our small airless room was not ideal for a siesta – whilst the walls were thick and the floors cool, the heat was inescapable.

***

Much later, after an early dinner of fried broad beans and a sinfully sweet rice pudding made with local honey, David and I managed to slip away on our own.

Strolling in the warm fragrant air of dusk, hands just touching, we blatantly disobeyed General Franco's rules about physical contact in public. At the end of the *Alameda* we leaned over the old walls of the ramparts still hot after the day's searing sun. Below us was the sheer rock face known as the Cauldron Handle. A patchwork of little rivers, all but dry after many months of summer drought, white houses and rows of olive and almond trees, stretched far away to the ring of mountains surrounding this beautiful town.

"David, I forgot to ask you, what did the bullfighter mean about Antonio's girlfriend?"

"We don't talk about it, but she killed herself by jumping into the Chorro gorge. She had her little dog in her arms. It was tragic for Antonio."

"What happened to make her do such a thing ?"

"Only she and Antonio know that. And sometimes I doubt if he really understands what drove her to it. Now I'm not going to waste our only evening together talking about other people."

We walked up the hill to the gardens of the Hotel Reina Victoria, green and cool, shaded by cypresses, pines and lofty palm trees which were a welcome change from the arid plains and barren mountains we had become used to.

"Ernest Hemingway lived here while he wrote of the art of bullfighting," David said as we sank into deep comfortable armchairs on the terrace, across a bottle of excellent Ronda red wine.

"I love it. It's so unexpected, hidden in the middle of these mountains. I can see why it attracts artists and writers. It's so dramatic here."

David nodded. "I've loved Ronda since the first time I came here two years ago. It has a magic about it that's difficult to describe."

We sat in companionable silence. Nervous of rejection, I hesitated to spoil the moment with talk of plans. After all, he hadn't really kissed me yet. Had I misread his attraction for me?

David broke the silence. "Look, I expect we're both short of cash but what are your plans after we get back to Álora? Are you serious about going to Granada? Perhaps we can go together."

My heart leapt with anticipation. But there was a small problem.

"David, I would love that, but I have to be back in Gibraltar to pick up my ship home."

David frowned. "I didn't know you had booked a passage. When's it for?"

"That's just the problem, my ship has no fixed date of arrival. She's en-route from Australia to Tilbury. But in theory I should have four days. Will that be long enough?"

David's brow furrowed. He took my hand. "I really want to spend some time with you."

"Me too; we never seem to be alone without John appearing. Look, we can pick up the bus back from Granada to Gibraltar, and we can find a really cheap *pension*."

"I should go to Huelva to finish my bull sketches, and I can do that from Gibraltar, so maybe we'll have time." David agreed.

We were about to leave when, to the strains of a guitar, a group of Murillo-type characters, dressed in black velvet jackets, knee breeches, black stockings and shoes, came out onto the terrace. It seemed a very hot outfit for an Andalucían summer evening.

"*Buenas noches*," the leader greeted us, waving his tambourine, as they launched into a spirited if somewhat tuneless version of *Granada*.

"They are students, called the *tuna*, and they make money to pay their study fees," David explained.

"Oh yes, I remember that Baron D'Avillier wrote that they are like troubadours and jugglers from the Middle Ages – poor and nomadic poets and musicians."

It was hard to talk over the music and the group had now progressed to singing a ballad about bandits and unrequited love, which seemed perfect for such a night in Ronda, the heart of banditry. Leaving the guitarist and flautist to continue playing, the leader with the tambourine shook it invitingly for payment from the hotel guests who had come out on to the terrace at the sound of the music. Apparently satisfied with the takings, they asked David for a request. We left to the tune of *Spanish Eyes*.

We walked slowly back to the *fonda* in the moonlight, enjoying the cool breeze, not daring to kiss in public, but just holding hands in the dark. My thoughts were turbulent – I ached for his touch.

CHAPTER TWENTY-SEVEN

Bandits

"I am almost certain to fall from a precipice into the bandit's arms." – Juliette de Robersart

The next day we left Ronda, bound for the Cueva de la Pileta. With David and Antonio at the head of our cavalcade, we left the town through the north entrance and headed towards the vast chain of mountains and the village of Montejaque. The countryside was beautiful with a scattering of white farmhouses ideally placed to offer shelter to bandits and smugglers.

Benjamin Disraeli wrote to his father in 1830:

> You will ask yourself how I can enjoy a life in which our pockets, and indeed our lives, are in constant danger, and which makes me more tired than I have ever been, since there are no roads and we travel on horseback at least eight hours a day, following a track which can only be compared to the sheer rocky bed of a dry waterfall, with no hope of rest or food. I will tell you in two words: the countryside is superb, its novelty unexpected... The mountain air, the rising sun, my increasing appetite, the picturesque variety of people and things that we come across, plus the imminent danger, make my life a delight.

The impression of danger and the prospect of an encounter with bandits was a recurring theme in his letters home.

Ronda, along with the Sierra Morena mountain range, was one of the most famous areas in the history of the Spanish bandit. The inhospitable mountains and isolated farmhouses made it easy for him to escape pursuit by the *Guardia Civil*. It was also on the route for all contraband being transported from Gibraltar to Córdoba, Seville or even to Madrid. There were, however, two very different types of *bandolero*. Whilst history has made them all appear romantic and gentlemanly – stealing from the rich to give to the poor allegedly this type of *bandolero* was in the minority. The vast majority were common thieves and murderers. I was searching for the gentlemen bandits and had no desire to meet up with a murderer on a dark road. Some were forced to ply their trade because of lack of work and the need to feed their families. Certainly after the War of Independence, many men returned home to find their lands ruined and no method of supporting their families. Rumours of the presence of any group of bandits in the vicinity struck terror into the hearts of the citizens, who could never be sure if they were from a gentlemanly or ungentlemanly band. Reports of the murder of those who refused to hand over their purses, and kidnappings for ransom of the rich and their children, terrified travellers with good reason. The bandits relied on the shepherds and local bar owners to warn them of any *Guardia Civil* in the vicinity and guaranteed their loyalty with stolen gold or jewellery.

Although many romantic authors were not so successful, Dundas Murray actually had an encounter with "two cut throat vagabonds, and I am sorry to spoil the romance, but they were rather out at the elbows, even though their steeds were capital". Murray and his companions managed to avoid being robbed, but the next travellers along the road were not so lucky and the "two vagabonds" relieved all the passengers in the coaches of all their belongings.

One traveller who had been assured that there were no more bandits in Andalucía, and therefore was travelling without a pistol, was held up. He believed that they were actors rehearsing for a play, until his money, clothes and horse disappeared into the distance with the "actors".

Disraeli, travelling from Córdoba one night, believed that at last he was to meet a bandit chief. The moon was rising, the group were nervous, and the horses, sensing the tension, pulled at their bits. Suddenly the guide heard the sound of horses in the distance. Disraeli remembered "a cold perspiration came over me. *Ave Maria!*" He drew up out of pure fear. "I had my purse ready for ransom." In this case the bandits really were a group of actors riding towards Córdoba.

Some of the bandits such as José Maria el Tempranillo (1805-1833) – so called because of his custom of rising early in the morning – were famous for their politeness to those they stopped. He was unfailingly courteous to women and is said to have always kissed the hand of a lady before removing her rings, saying, "such a pretty hand does not need a ring". He always ensured that ladies were comfortably seated in the shade before pillaging their luggage. Known as "the gentleman bandit", he was the famous leader of a band of some fourteen *bandoleros*, well disciplined and organized.

José Maria has gone down in history as the greatest of the romantic bandits. It was said that King Fernando VII was the King of Spain and José Maria the Master of Andalucía. His father was killed when he was just a young child, leaving his mother destitute. The village priest helped them and tried unsuccessfully to give the young José Maria a basic education. As with most bandits, he was illiterate and very superstitious. Most of them wore some sort of amulet for protection. José Maria wore a medallion with the image of the Virgin of Sorrows of Córdoba, whom he trusted to keep him safe.

An affair of the heart condemned him to life as an outlaw. The local village fair was the only opportunity during the year to dance with a girl. José Maria was dancing with Clara when one of his neighbours tried to muscle in.

"She only dances with me," declared the young man. An argument ensued. José Maria stabbed his rival in the stomach, fled to the mountains and began a long and successful career as a "good" bandit.

The *Guardia Civil* were always on his trail, and laid a trap to capture him. He received a message that his beautiful young gypsy wife, Maria Jeronima, was about to give birth to his son. Leaving the rest of his group he rode his horse, Beata, alone to the farmhouse, where the *guardia* were hiding in waiting. In the ensuing gunfire Maria Jeronima was killed. José Maria placed the newborn baby in his cummerbund, his dead wife across the front of his saddle and galloped out unscathed through a hail of bullets. He left his baby son with his grandmother in the neighbouring town of Grazalema and buried his wife in the cemetery. Some days later, the child was baptised and José Maria appeared at the church. Although it was common knowledge that he was in the town, the *Guardia Civil* turned a blind eye, and to the fury of their superiors in Madrid, the bandit was allowed to return to his mountain hideout.

When a common thief, posing as José Maria, stopped a carriage and robbed a lady violently, the bandit was so outraged that he pursued the man and killed him. He returned the ladies' belongings with the message, 'José Maria El Tempranillo does not hurt ladies.'

Within a few years he commanded all the major routes in Andalucía. He stole valuable breeding stallions from a cavalry depot, and a coach-load of cigars destined for the royal palace in Madrid. In one hold-up on the Madrid Road he took a great number of prisoners. José Maria ordered a sheep from a neighbouring field to be slaughtered and they all sat down to lunch together, bandits and prisoners. After the meal, several of the young unmarried female captives offered to remain as hostages if the married women could be spared and allowed to return home. José Maria was so impressed by their generosity that he not only returned their property but gave them presents as a memento of their adventure.

He never forgot a favour. A muleteer had lost his only belonging, his mule. Desperate and about to end his problems by jumping from the bridge into the River Guadalquivir, his wife rushed to stop him.

"We're saved, Pepe, don't jump. Look at this."

In her hands was a small box of gold coins, delivered by one of the bandits' men, with the message "José Maria helps those who help him". The previous year Pepe, the muleteer, had helped the bandit to escape from his pursuers, and the favour had been returned.

CHAPTER
TWENTY-EIGHT

Bandit Tales

"The profession (of gentleman bandit) is popular in the lower classes – because of the power, show of bravery and the prospect of quick riches. The luxury, the songs, the smiles of beautiful women, the feasting and the attraction of a free life and camaraderie give it an irresistible fascination for an energetic fighting people with a rich imagination." – Richard Ford

As we rode, I was lost in my thoughts of bandits, imagining the characters who had once been on this trail. David interrupted my reverie.

"Let me guess, that dreamy look on your face tells me you are thinking about bandits?"

"You're right, don't you think this is perfect countryside for an ambush?"

"You do realise that some of them were just thugs.? Have you heard of José Ulloa? He's better known as *Tragabuches*.

"No."

"Well he was a bullfighter, singer and a semi-retired smuggler, and he agreed to join a friend in a bullfight in Málaga so they set off on horseback. However, close to the village of El Burgo, his horse threw him and his arm was broken. Being superstitious, he considered that the fall was fate and that he was not supposed to fight the bulls that day. He returned home unexpectedly to find his front door locked. When it was finally opened, he found his wife, Maria "La Nena" naked and trembling. His suspicions aroused, he searched the house. He found nothing out of order. Groaning with pain from his broken arm, he went to the big earthenware water pot in the corner of the kitchen to drink. The ladle appeared to be blocked by a foreign object in the giant pot. José put his hand into the water and touched the top of a man's head. His wife, a gypsy flamenco dancer, had spent the afternoon in bed with Pepe, the adolescent sacristan of the local church."

"What did he do?"

"Well, in a fit of rage the jealousy he knifed the sacristan in the neck. Blood spurted from the wound and the sacristan's body sank under a wave of bloody bubbles. Maria ran for the stairs; he grabbed her round the waist and, with his broken arm, he lifted her from the ground.

"He opened the balcony window and threw his screaming wife over the railings to the ground below, where she lay still. Calmly he went down to the street where his wife's body lay in the dust. He decorously arranged her clothing and pulled the hair away from her face. His bullfighting career over, he rode to the mountains where he joined the group of bandits known as the Seven Children of Écija. So you see not all bandits were perfect gentlemen."

"OK, but that was a crime of passion – he loved his wife."

"That makes it alright then does it?" he laughed.

CHAPTER TWENTY-NINE

En route to the Caves

"Like a cathedral or a sacred place offered by nature to God. The water is purer than holy water; the bubbling waterfalls are notes from the most melodic of organs."
– William George Clark

"These roads are appalling," John complained. "I don't know how the horses don't lose more shoes."

"That's why we carry spares that Pitirri can put on in an emergency," Antonio told him. "Luckily, as you've seen, we travel mainly on dirt tracks which are usually in better condition than the roads, and easier on the horses' feet."

The labourers charged with keeping the dangerous roads in good repair were to be seen lounging on the roadside, cigarettes in mouths, with baskets of stones and pickaxes over their shoulders. Alexandre Dumas complained about the potholes: "May heaven grant me, in my old age, the boon of becoming a Spanish road mender, whose great mission in life is to swathe himself in his cloak and watch travellers suffer."

In return for a small wage and a roadside house they toiled very slowly and unenthusiastically at their task and seemed to make very little impression on the monstrous potholes that appeared round every corner of the roads.

D'Avillier wrote:

> The Spanish road-mender spends his entire life at leisure in smoking and is careful to labour as little as he possibly can. Who is the traveller who has not seen him slowly transport his small wicker basket (the wheelbarrow being unknown) of earth or pebbles, and, arrived at the end of his journey, carefully deposit its fearfully inadequate contents in some yawning rut which he at times succeeds in filling up?

"Many of the men you see were Republican sympathisers," Antonio told us in a low voice. "This way they get punished, the roads get mended, after a fashion, and it doesn't cost the country too much."

We stopped to refresh the horses and ourselves at a *cantina* in Montejaque. The village had the appearance of having slid down into the valley from the impressive craggy peaks above, and being almost inaccessible even to mountain goats. It is divided to all intents and purposes into two parts, the old Arab settlement with narrow winding streets and the lower, more modern part of the town.

We were ravenous, so we remounted and David and Antonio led us off in search of the village of Benaoján and lunch.

"These flies really bite," John swatted at his arm. "Look, I'm coming up in great itchy lumps."

"Try lemon juice when we get to the village," advised David. "They don't like it. Or drink more beer, it seems to give the blood a strange taste. Let me tell you a story about a cat, to take your mind off your bites," he went on.

"You notice that the soil here is mainly limestone. This creates underground rivers and several large caves have been found over the years. One in particular is the La Cueva del Gato. We won't actually visit it or we'll be late at the Cave of La Pileta, which is much more interesting." Ignoring John's grumbles, David continued. "The shape of the entrance resembles a cat. They also say that when the cave was discovered, a cat was put into the fissure where the stream disappears into the mountain. The unfortunate animal finally found its way through the cavern and reappeared at the entrance to the cave."

"Well cat references aside, they say it's a very beautiful ride," I said.

"Have you read the book of the travels of Josephine Brinckmann? I found it in a library in England.

She was an intrepid French lady travelling in 1850, accompanied by the mayor of Benaoján, and an armed escort of two soldiers from the garrison in Gibraltar. She described the route to the cave as 'sheer mountain paths across the most picturesque region that one could dream of'. But the route from Benaoján to Málaga was considered to be so dangerous that she was sent a further armed guard by the officer in charge of the garrison in Ronda."

We made our way carefully along the mountainside with a sheer precipice on the right-hand side, hoping that nothing would distract our horses from their careful descent. The grey, inhospitable crags, bereft of all plant life but wild lavender and thyme, reminded me of Doré's beautiful black and white illustrations. Large black birds circled overhead. I hoped they wouldn't frighten the horses. Susan and Platero were close behind me and I could hear her berating him for not concentrating. I put my trust in Krishna and gave him his head. He snorted nervously but did not stumble on the rocky path.

"If we had time we could climb down to the bottom of the ravine and follow the river through the mountain to the Cueva del Gato, but only now in the summer. The river's too deep in winter."

"How long would it take, David?" asked Andrew.

"I have never done it but I am told about seven hours."

Andrew grinned. "Perhaps I'll give it a miss this time."

We entered the small bar in the village square at Benaojan, cool and fragrant with cooking smells of meat and herbs. A delicious stew of rabbit and sloppy rice was served from a huge cauldron steaming on an open fire in the patio behind the bar by Consuelo, a beaming, dark-skinned lady.

Susan picked at the bones.

"This could well be cat," she whispered. "I'm becoming an expert at spotting stewed moggie, but I'm so hungry I don't care. It tastes delicious."

***

David was anxious to move on to the Cave of La Pileta so we reluctantly braved the heat of the afternoon to rejoin the horses. Not one local was to be seen; they were very sensibly staying behind their tightly closed shutters. Only mad dogs and Englishmen would be out in the sun at that hour. Even the horses seemed to wilt as we left the shade of the river bank and continued west through the wheat fields. The harvest was over and the sheaves of wheat stacked up awaiting the mules who would take them to the winnowing ground. Cattle and hobbled mules grazed on the stubble. We entered a cork oak forest and were grateful for the shade, although the ground was rough and made difficult going for the horses.

A few kilometres further on we came across a mule train. The muleteers were harvesting the cork, and loading it on the waiting animals. The little donkeys almost disappeared under the heavy loads, and the sturdier mules fared better. Pigs grazed on the acorns under the trees, hampering the harvesters and causing some colourful language.

As the air cooled slightly, we started to climb a rough track to our right and with the little village of Benajaon below us in the valley, it seemed we had reached our destination.

CHAPTER THIRTY

The Cave of La Pileta

There was neither a visible entrance nor sign of the cave's existence, but Pitirri jumped off his horse and rang a large cowbell beside the track. From a little farmhouse in the valley below emerged a slim figure who hollered back and began the steep climb up the hillside to where we waited. It was Tomás Bullón, son of the man who discovered the cave. A few moments later, he bounded over a rock, startling the horses as he landed on the track. Tomás was a cheerful, good-looking young man, and was to act as our guide.

He, Antonio and David embraced – Spanish-style, with much back slapping.

"*Hola*, how was the journey?" asked Tomás.

"Hot as hell," David told him.

"You'll find it cooler in the caves," Tomás told us, as he unlocked the big iron door.

"OK, we need to leave the horses with Pitirri."

Whilst the rest of us dismounted, Tomás hastened to help Susan who appeared to have caught his eye. We tethered the horses and gathered at the cave mouth. Tomás gave us each a paraffin lamp.

"Look where these lamps are made." Andrew showed us his lamp and we laughed to see that they were stamped "Made in Belfast, Ireland".

"The Spanish lamps are gasoline, and too dangerous in the caves," David explained.

"Take care, it's very slippery," Tomás warned.

He gave Susan his hand. Andrew helped me down the steps and John, as usual, looked after himself and his cameras.

Tomás told us that his father, José, had found the cave in 1905, when he was searching for bat droppings to fertilize his fields. He had noticed that great flocks of bats would leave the caves each night, and knew the mountain had always been known as the 'ridge of the bats'. One day, he took a rope and descended about 30 metres into the cave. Once there he saw piles of bones, which were not of animals that had fallen into the caves, but had obviously been carried inside. By the light of his acetylene lamp he also saw little pieces of ceramic on the ground and had the sensation that this cave in the bowels of the earth had been used by many people. He saw black markings on the walls and strange letters. His discovery was to change the course of his life, although at that time he knew nothing of prehistoric culture.

Days later he returned to the cave and climbed a waterfall. He discovered a chink of natural light that filtered into another cavern and found a cemetery full of human and animal remains, and more ceramics. He came upon a skeleton in the foetal position. Drawings in red and black covered the walls.

Although this story, along with the bats, made me slightly apprehensive about journeying deeper into the cave, the rest of the group seemed anxious to see the paintings. As we moved on, I hoped that the it was true that bats could only see in the dark.

We followed Tomás and Susan. David brought up the rear and with nervous laughter we all descended into the dark cavern.

The caves were named *pileta*, or small basin, after the Roman basin that was found at the other end of the valley on the edge of the road. It is thought that the Roman legions who passed to and from Ronda used it to refresh themselves on their journey.

At the bottom of the slope was the Labyrinth – a series of small passage ways down which we fitted with difficulty. We finally passed into a larger cave with black drawings on the walls. Our lanterns illuminated the tremendous height of the cavern.

Down we went again to an immense cave. "Raise your lanterns," called Tomás, "look at the paintings." We saw by, the light of the lanterns, paintings of horses, deer, bulls, and an enormous fish. "The experts say that some of the animals were painted by left handed artists."

"How did the previous inhabitants see to do such accurate paintings, in the corners of the caves? Without these lamps it's pitch dark," Andrew puzzled.

"We think that they soaked pine branches in animal fat and used them for heating and lighting."

Tomás pointed out some stalagmites where small holes had been carved, probably to support some type of candle. There were stains where the animal grease had run down the rocks.

"It's really warm," Susan wiped sweat from her forehead. "Aren't caves usually cold?"

"The temperature never changes from fifteen degrees centigrade down here," Tomás explained.

Everything felt clammy, and he told us the humidity was usually a hundred per cent. The cave was originally formed by an underground river. During the dry months the stalactites were formed but in the winter torrents of water raged through the caverns.

Then we met the bats. As we passed into the next cramped cave, David called out, "Shine your lanterns on the roof," and there, in a heaving, writhing mass, were the bats. Millions of small, squeaking, furry bodies with webbed feet. My skin crawled and my mouth was dry with terror. There was no escape for me when, disturbed by the light of our lanterns, they took flight directly towards us, swooping through the narrow passageway. To the amusement of the rest of the party, I threw myself and my lantern on the floor in complete panic, closed my eyes, put my hands over my head and prayed no low-flying bat would touch me. No amount of positive thinking could persuade me that they were more scared than I was.

"You could have warned me, you rat," I gasped, when the bats had passed, furious at my irrational exhibition of fear and David's laughter.

"I didn't realise that you were *so* scared," he tried not to laugh and to look solicitous as he helped me up and recovered my lantern. "I'm really sorry."

I had seen enough of dark caverns and bats to last me a lifetime but we still had a long climb to the end of the cave. We passed a stalactite known as the Leaning Tower of Pisa, and through another large cave with a painting of a goat, a pregnant mare, and a fish.

"The different colours of the paintings shows that they were done at different times. Yellow, red, and black were used by different civilizations," David told us.

I stumbled and almost fell, tripping on the uneven floor. Many centuries of winter floods had carved their way through the lower caves, leaving deep gullies that were difficult to see in the dim light of the lanterns.

Tomás raised his lantern to show us a beautiful painting of a bearded goat.

"Look, here you can see the marks of the giant cave bear. The bears hibernated here and must have had fights with the cavemen. You can see that they were over three metres tall and the cave men were very small. The bears also had the advantage of being able to see in the dark. But I have kept the best till last." Tomás led us to a small gallery where an almost perfectly preserved skeleton of a young woman lay on the floor. "There were four skeletons," he told us, "but two were sent to Madrid and one crumbled when we tried to move it."

"Why were they here?" asked Andrew, "it seems the most difficult part of the cave to get to?"

"The scientists thought that perhaps it was here that they prepared sacrifices to the gods. But it appears that there was a powerful earthquake about six thousand years ago, and it is possible that the exits from the cave were blocked and these four young women were trapped."

I shuddered with a sudden chill as the hairs on my arms stood up. What a way to die, alone and in the dark, and surrounded by fluttering bats.

More than two hours after we had entered, we stumbled out into the bright sun, and I heaved a sigh of relief.

Tomás passed round cold drinks as we sat in the shade to recover from the long climb out of the cave.

"My father was passionate about the cave," he told us. "A French Jesuit, Henri Breuil, visited in 1912, and he told my father, 'Never permit anybody to damage the cave. The paintings are a treasure without price'. But the news of the findings spread and many thought that the cave might hold gold hidden by the cave's prehistoric inhabitants."

Tomás told us of the many nights when, alerted by the barking of their dogs, his father had to climb fast up the steep slope to the cave's entrance to stop trespassers from entering and damaging the priceless contents of the cavern. People the family had considered friends attempted, by foul means and fair, to persuade them to sell the ownership of the land so that it could be exploited commercially. They did not understand that the family wanted to protect the cave at all costs, and felt that this could only happen if they retained the ownership and rights over the cave. The promise that José Bullon made to Breuil, to care for the cave, was kept.

The bones of one of the human skeletons had been sent to London to the British Museum for analysis.

"We will certainly visit them when we get home," Susan enthused.

"Sadly," said Tomás, "many of the other remains were taken to Spanish museums and have been sold to private collections. But I am glad you will be able to see some of them with your own eyes."

CHAPTER
THIRTY-ONE

Rancho Harillo

"The Spaniards possess a great variety of talents, but plumbing is not one of them." – Penelope Chetwode

We took the reins from Pitirri and Sebastian and, leading the horses, we slowly and carefully descended into the valley towards the farmhouse, where Tomás's mother, Teresa, awaited us. She was a handsome dark-haired woman, but the flecks of grey and deeply lined face showed the hardships of survival in the mountains.

"Welcome, Antonio. And you David. Did you have a long ride today?"

"Only from Ronda, but it was very hot. Thank goodness it's cooling down now."

The Rancho de Harillo was an attractive, long, low, white building where, as usual, the animals were accommodated on one side and the people on the other. Clay tiles and shuttered windows kept the main room cool in the lingering heat of the day. The sleeping arrangements were two big dormitories, one for the men and one for women, separated by a curtain. Mattresses were laid on the floor and stacked in the corner were the farming tools and racks of potatoes and onions.

Susan and I unloaded our saddlebags and, having chosen our mattresses, followed Teresa as she beckoned us outside, carrying our clean clothes and toilet bags – I badly wanted that long cold shower. However, Susan and I were to discover that the plumbing was even more rudimentary here than in the *posadas*.

"Come, just you two girls."

Teresa led us outside to a trench dug behind the stables and gave us a long handled spade and a bucket of water drawn from the well. The trench was the lavatory department, and the bucket the shower.

Laughing at our confusion, she said, "Ladies go first and then the men."

So much for that icy cold shower I had dreamed of. Although we had become accustomed to the lack of privacy after a week on the road, this was pretty basic. Neither did the single-sex dormitories offer much privacy for my budding romance with David. I despaired of ever being really alone with him.

We all made the best of our allotted bucket of water and settled into our dormitory. It was clean and there seemed to be no wildlife either of the mouse or flea variety. Later, sitting on the front terrace sipping sweet muscatel wine and watching the evening light over the mountains, showers didn't seem so important. Tomas and Susan had disappeared, ostensibly to visit the mules, and returned wearing very sheepish grins just in time for dinner. I was dying to get the full story from her later.

Teresa had done us proud and we all clustered round the table for a meal of chicken and chickpeas flavoured with rancid *jamon serrano* bones and home-grown vegetables. Rice pudding, sickly with condensed milk, was a popular end to the meal. Tired after the long day, our travelling companions bade us goodnight.

"Shall we take a walk?"

David uncurled his long legs from the rocking chair. I had blisters from the long trek through the cave in leather riding boots, but the opportunity to be alone together was too good to miss.

The bats were still swooping as we walked slowly hand in hand down the valley through the stand of poplar trees, talking of the cave and the day's ride. Out of sight of the house, we climbed down to the bed of the stream, which had almost dried out in the summer heat. Only a few small pools remained. My blisters were throbbing.

"I need to take my boots off, my feet are really sore and those pools look perfect."

I sat down on the grassy bank.

"Can you give my boots a pull?"

He did so and the water was blissfully cool on my aching feet, as I paddled up the stream.

"Did nobody tell you about leeches?" teased David

"Are you serious? What do they look like?"

I jumped out of the water.

"They look like small black slugs, and they suck your blood," said David with relish.

"One of Antonio's dogs got one stuck in its throat after drinking from the river. We couldn't understand why it had blood pouring from its mouth. The usual remedy is to put wet tobacco on the leech and it will release its grip. We had to pour a pounded-up cigarette down the poor dog's throat, but it worked."

By the light of the moon I examined between my toes for little black animals.

"Can I be of any help?"

David pushed me gently down onto the grass and teasingly ran his fingers through my hair.

"I don't think the leeches are in my hair, but there's no harm in checking."

I pulled his face down to mine and kissed him slowly on the corner of his mouth. My heart was thudding.

"I can't find any leeches," he smiled wickedly, "but I'll keep looking."

The grass was cool on my back. He gently kissed my neck and my eyes and finally our lips met. I felt overwhelmed as his hands moved up under my shirt and caressed my breast and I fumbled with his belt.

Suddenly David groaned and rolled away from me.

"We can't do this, Jill, we must stop."

"Stop what?" I mumbled as I rolled over and pinned his arms and nuzzled his chest. "We've only just started."

He sat up and smiled down at me, stroking my hair.

"Stop looking for leeches. Look, I really want to make love to you but we must be careful. I don't want to upset Antonio."

"Why would it upset him?"

"Because if the *Guardia Civil* happened to find us we would be in very hot water. They are not going to believe that we are looking for leeches in your hair, and don't forget that this sort of thing is illegal in Spain. He would be held responsible for our behaviour." He bent down and kissed me, slowly and tenderly. His chin was rough and masculine against my skin and he smelled faintly of a mixture of garlic and cologne.

"I'm sorry to sound so sensible and unromantic, but another thing is that I've got no contraception. Do you?"

"No, It's not the sort of thing I usually travel with."

"They're prohibited in Spain. I'll try and get hold of some under the counter."

In my head I knew he was right but my body was deaf to logic.

"We'll be together in Granada – I think we'll just have to wait till then."

Reluctantly I pulled my boots on and we tidied ourselves up, removing twigs and leaves from our clothes and hair. We returned slowly to the farmhouse, savouring a final kiss under a spreading olive tree, before separating to our respective dormitories to toss and turn in the hot and sticky night air, dreaming of what might have been.

CHAPTER THIRTY-TWO

Mules and An Encounter with the *Guardia Civil*

"The land of the proud steed and the stubborn mule."
– George Borrow

Next morning, having done battle with the sanitary arrangements, and eaten a large breakfast of Teresa's fresh eggs fried in an enormous pan of olive oil with crispy fried bread, we loaded up the horses for the return to Ronda.

Tomas and Susan still had stars in their eyes and were struggling to understand each other's language. This greatly amused Teresa, who said she had never seen her son so taken with a girl. It seemed Tomas was to come to Ronda that evening on the donkey when he had finished his work at the cave.

Because Antonio had gone to Seville until the evening to attend to some business, David was our guide. Pitirri broke into song as we left Benaojan, probably inspired by Tomas's infatuation with Susan, and sang endlessly of robbers, young love, and death in the afternoon. Eventually David told him to give it a rest.

We took a shorter route towards Ronda, along the river, splashing through the pools, startling small turtles and frogs. A heron rose lazily into the air, complaining at the interruption.

"Look," Susan whispered, "a kingfisher." Above our heads he sat on a branch, intent on his fishing, unfazed by our passage. We paused for a drink and a *tapa* in a small roadside bar.

A few kilometres from Ronda we met up again with our friends the muleteers with their loads of cork. Even the mules were now scarcely visible under the heavy loads as they plodded resolutely up the narrow paths ahead of us, encouraged by the muleteers, *los arrieros*, so-called from the verb *arrear*, to encourage. They berated any lazy member of the train with "*arre mulo, burro*". Directed by voice rather than a stick, the mules and donkeys would obey.

The muleteers rode comfortably on the big panniers woven from *esparto* grass, their legs round the mule's neck, and we spotted one who was sleeping face-down along the animal's back, lulled by the monotonous swaying motion. The backbone of the Spanish economy, mule trains were, for many years, the only method of transporting goods due to the appalling condition of the roads. Carts did not last long on the stony and potholed tracks. Cork, straw, acorns, wood, all had to be loaded onto the mules, using the grass panniers. Dried fish and fruit were transported from village to village. Fish was brought up from the coast and the *cosarios* – delivery men – tied their mules up to a handy window bar in a village and spread their wares on the ground. Materials, ribbons, clothes, shoes and men's boots, all arrived by mule.

Washington Irving in the middle of the nineteenth century described his encounter with a mule train:

> It is very picturesque to come across a line of muleteers in a mountain pass. Firstly the sound of the lead mules breaking the silence of the hills with their melody, or the voice of the muleteer shouting to a lazy or straying animal, or singing with all his might. Finally one sees the mules describing a low zigzag up the sharp pass or descending such steep cliffs that they are outlined against the horizon.

The lead mule would usually wear a coloured pompon on her head collar and a bell around her neck to define her superiority in the long-eared hierarchy. Always known as Capitana, and always female, she would be chosen for her experience and docility. She took the lead and the others obeyed, instinctively following the age-old, familiar tracks.

Gautier remarked that the mules were "so thin and shaved so that they resemble so many enormous mice".

George Borrow saw muleteers as "sullen, proud and rarely courteous – true lords of the routes of Spain". Whilst Ennenpreis, a Swedish traveller, in 1926 described them as; "lazy, lying in the sun. They have nothing, need nothing, are rich in their poverty and happy in their simplicity."

The well-being of his animals was all-important to the devoted *arriero*. He attended to their needs before his own and slept on the ground beside them in the *posada*. They were, after all, his livelihood. If travellers were caught in bad weather in the mountains they knew they could place their trust in the *arrieros* and their mules to lead them to safety. Many a lost and lonely rider has heard in the mist and rain the echo of the *arrieros* singing – of love and legend, *boleros* and *fandangos* – and known that they could count on his help and company. Ford said, "The mule in Spain is like a camel in the East and has a similar temperament to his owner – willing and stubborn, resigned to his burden and stoic in his work, and his tiredness and privations."

Gautier maintained that "In the mountains a mule is really intractable and feels its importance and takes advantage of this. He frequently stops to call to his friends with horrible inarticulate sighs, convulsive sobs and a frightful clicking resembling the shrieks of a child who is being murdered."

Our pace was slowed by the mule train ahead of us, the track too narrow to pass them. Whilst still some miles from Ronda, we came once again upon a patrol of those unpopular guardians of the countryside, the *Guardia Civil*. Mounted on two large bay horses, they blocked the track ahead of us, threatening and impassive, wearing their shiny black tricorn hats with the flap at the back to keep out the sun.

Having fruitlessly examined the muleteers' loads at length for contraband, they turned their attention to us.

"Documents!" barked the sergeant.

We delved into our saddlebags and produced our passports. Pitirri and Sebastian handed over their identity documents and we all waited nervously as our papers were examined with such care that it was obvious that our sergeant had no idea what they were. However, our photos obviously passed muster and we heaved a sigh of relief as he handed them back with an air of disappointment.

Now it was the turn of the horses. With much solemnity the papers were perused and the horses' descriptions, colour and age were checked against our mounts. It seemed that it was with some reluctance that they finally remounted and let us pass with a, "Go with God".

Andrew heaved a sigh of relief. "They seem to be pretty unpleasant and they have a lot of power."

"They were originally set up to help stamp out the bandits and robbers that operated on the Spanish roads. They're now a feared and repressive police force. It's not a good idea to mess about with them. They are housed in police barracks with their families, and they serve far from their native towns to avoid fraternization with the locals. In rural areas, their job is to know everything about everyone. The officers wield as much power as the village priest or the mayor."

An ominous clinking of metal on stone warned me that Krishna was about to lose a shoe.

"David, listen to that. It's a front shoe I think."

Luckily Pitirri had come prepared with spares of all sizes, but we needed to find a blacksmith to shoe him. We all paused whilst Pitirri and Sebastian removed the loose shoe and nails, which would do more harm than good and, since we were only about three kilometres away from Ronda, decided to continue slowly on our way. Soon we could see the town above us to our left, surrounded by cactus and aloes. A Moorish poet, Ibn Sa'id, wrote in the fifteenth century, "The fortress of Ronda uses the clouds as a turban and the sweet water of the rivers as necklaces."

As we rode through the valley, I marvelled at the beauty of this town and agreed with the earlier travellers that life in Spain is different. An anonymous American traveller wrote, "What a country is Spain for a traveller, where the most miserable inn is as full of adventure as an enchanted castle and every meal is in itself an achievement."

We rode through the town and over the bridge, accompanied by the usual troop of children and dogs. By now Krishna was beginning to feel his sore hoof and I dismounted and walked up the last hill to the *posada*. Pitirri was to send Sebastian for the blacksmith, who would also check the rest of the horses for loose or worn shoes. We retired to the *fonda* for a luxurious cold shower before supper.

***

Refreshed, we met for a drink in a little tapas bar. Antonio had returned from Seville and we all sat at a table looking across at the bullring watching the world of Ronda.

Supper was ready at the *fonda* and no sooner were we seated than Tomás appeared on his donkey, having ridden from the Cueva de la Pileta in search of Susan. It must have taken him several hours. He refused food but accepted a beer whilst Susan, who was starving as usual, kept him waiting whilst she did justice to a large bowl of potato and partridge stew. Finally she pushed back her chair and, hiding a broad smile, she whispered to me behind her hand, "Don't forget it does them good to wait."

They bade goodnight to everyone and disappeared towards the old town. David and I were both tired and decided to find a quiet bar for a cup of coffee before an early bed.

When I reached my room Susan had not yet returned. No doubt she was still with Tomás.

CHAPTER
THIRTY-THREE

Goodbye to Ronda

"Terrifying precipices and threatening mountains, foaming torrents, shady oaks and alcornoque forests."
– Charles Rochfort-Scott

We bade farewell sadly to Ronda and headed towards the village of El Burgo. I had, from vanity, decided not to wear a hat the previous day and was now suffering from sunstroke. The motion of the horse made me nauseous and the only other option was to walk and lead my mount. Krishna's hoof seemed to have recovered but was probably all the better for not having to carry my weight. Andalucían riding boots are not made for stumbling for hours down dry riverbeds and up steep rocky slopes, and I already had blisters from walking through the caves in my boots.

When my blistered feet became too painful, I had no option but to mount again, and spend a miserable day feeling sorry for myself, snapping at my companions and missing David, who had remained in Ronda to make contact with a bull breeder in Huelva. The dazzling intensity of the light made my head hurt.

Travelling in 1852 George John Cayley wrote in "The Bridle Roads of Spain" that the potholed tracks were "dreadful roads through a wild district". As we slowly descended from the Ronda mountains and took our route along the river valley, groups of red-legged partridges scattered at our approach, spooking the horses with their raucous danger calls. We took the southern route through the mountains – riding down gently sloping hillsides planted with olive trees where little brown owls blinked at us from the branches. Their plumage made them almost invisible; if John hadn't pointed them out we would not have seen them.

As we squeezed through a narrow pass in the overhanging rocks, two skinny grey foxes stood on the path in front of us – motionless – before disappearing into the undergrowth hoarsely barking their defiance.

In some ways it was a relief to leave the high mountains of the Serranía de Ronda, and certainly it was easier on the horses. We were all pleased when in the late afternoon, after the longest day yet in the saddle, we reached our destination.

I recalled Gautier's description of El Burgo as a "miserable village" but it seemed very attractive after such a long ride, and it looked very romantic perched on the hilltop surrounded by its hedge of prickly pears. The *posada* reminded me of a description by one traveller:

> A *posada* is a strange cavern which you ride into and
> is not exactly a stable yard, a coach house, a kitchen
> or a lumber yard but something of all.

Everything that might conceivably come in useful at some time in the future was stored in the big central patio. The stables were already occupied by a mule train that was transporting olive oil to the coast. The *arrieros* were busy frying up large quantities of bread, oil and garlic in the *posada* kitchen and I was glad that Antonio had decided we were to eat in the local bar that night.

***

El Burgo (which in Moorish means 'a fortress') is situated on a hilltop 500 metres above sea level, which gave it a big advantage in dealing with invading forces. It is surrounded by an almost impassable barrier of prickly pear bushes. With its source in the Sierra de las Nieves far above Ronda, the River Turon, which separates the two halves of the town, also gave the Moors an unusual advantage in that they were able to draw water from inside the castle, thus enabling them to withstand a siege for longer than normal. The river flows down the oleander-filled valley towards El Chorro and Ardales. Poplars and weeping willows line its banks and the cries of bee-eaters fill the air. El Burgo was of great importance in Roman times as a staging point on the road from Acinipo to Ronda. The remains of the original bridge used by the Roman legions can still be seen, although it was rebuilt in the eighteenth century. In 1910 the American Abel Chapman wrote of two Spains to be discovered by the traveller:

> Pathless solitudes, desolate steppe and prairie, marsh and mountain, majestic sierras, or a land overflowing with historic and artistic interest, memorials of mediaeval romance and stirring times when wave after wave of successive conquest swept the Peninsula.

El Burgo was famous for the caves in which snow was kept during the winter to be transported to the coast to keep food and drink cool in the hot summer months. Electricity was unavailable still in many areas, and fridges had to be filled with blocks of snow. The snow was collected and transported by mule or donkey to the men who, using a wooden crusher, pressed it into the holes in the ground, forming the ice blocks. The ice was then covered with brushwood and earth until the early summer. In the cool early morning the blocks of ice were dug out, loaded onto donkeys or mules and taken to Yunquera. The lanterns sparkled like stars as the men and mules struggled down the icy slopes. They would load the blocks of ice into grass panniers. Each loaded pannier, weighing fifty kilos, was then harnessed onto the beasts of burden that carried it over the rocky and dangerous tracks to the towns. The ice took two days to reach the coast, the muleteers sleeping in the *posadas* en route. Most of the men had few clothes to keep out the intense cold of the Sierra de las Nieves, and only grass sandals for their feet.

The caves round El Burgo were known as the haunt of the "last" bandit to inhabit the area, Pasos Largos, 'was so-called because his father was very tall. His real name was Juan Mingolla. He hunted and lived from selling the game he killed, and was imprisoned for poaching.

Aged 43, he became a fugitive but was much loved by the local people, and had friends in all the countryside. Local farmers would invite him to eat with their family out of compassion for his loneliness. Finally, the law caught up with him.

A single shot echoed round the mountains in the early morning mist and startled red-legged partridges rose screeching from the rocks around the cave.

The shiny black tricorns of the *Guardia Civil* peered out from the rocks where their owners had taken cover and the young lieutenant raised his hand, cautioning his men to remain still. Scrubby wild olive and mountain oak trees obscured his view of the mouth of the cave.

"*Basta ya*, that's enough. Come out, Juan Mingolla, you are surrounded. *Mierda*," he swore as his foot slipped on the steep rock face and dislodged a shower of small stones, startling the police horses tethered below them.

He was cold and tired of this game of hide and seek. A warm bed and a young compliant wife awaited him in the village if only this tiresome bandit would realise he was beaten. Irritably, he fired a single shot in the air.

"Throw out your weapon, it's your last chance."

Through the swirling mist the figure of a man appeared at the mouth of the cave.

"Don't shoot, it's me, Jose. Juan Mingolla is dead."

The body of the bandit lay in his mountain hideout, betrayed by his erstwhile friend, Jose, in exchange for a purse full of gold; and promotion for the ambitious young lieutenant, who just happened to be the traitor's brother.

CHAPTER
THIRTY-FOUR

Don't Mix Your Drinks

"For a bad night a mattress of wine."
– Spanish proverb

Susan and I shared a room with four iron beds. As usual there was no glass in the windows but the breeze dispersed the garlic fumes from the *arrieros'* supper, and the cool mountain air was very welcome. David had arrived and he and Antonio were already discussing the day's ride over a beer in the bar opposite the *posada*. My heart did its usual lurch when I saw him and with indecent haste I went over to the bar and grabbed the chair next to him.

"How was the day?" he asked.

"Long and hot," I groaned.

"Fascinating birds," John said happily.

"How did you get here, David?" asked Andrew arriving and reaching for a chair.

"I had a great journey. I hitched a lift with charming old man and his coachman who were travelling to Málaga in a carriage pulled by four black mares. I tied my horse to the back of the carriage and spent a delightful day travelling in comfort and discussing horses. He was kind enough to drop me off at the door of the *posada*."

That would have suited me much better than getting more blisters and walking for miles on what Théophile Gautier described as "impassable roads in an infernal heat". However, a glass of excellent Ronda red wine and the prospect of a good meal in David's company raised my spirits.

Susan was fretting about Tomás.

"I don't think I'll see him again. How's he going to get here?" With only two days left before the end of our holiday it seemed unlikely, especially since he couldn't leave the cave for more than a day at a time. "Even if I write there's nobody to translate the letter for him. I'll just have to get started on Spanish lessons as I soon as I get back."

It seemed as if Susan's fiancé was out of the picture. For once I decided that I would bite my tongue until she decided to discuss the problem.

Supper was delicious *gazpacho* followed by stewed goat (advertised by José the barman as kid), which appeared to have walked almost as many miles as we had that day. It was served with beans and vegetables in a giant round earthenware bowl, which José placed proudly in the middle of the table, and was extremely tasty, but nevertheless a strong set of teeth were needed to deal with the fibrous lumps. Antonio told us it had only been slaughtered that afternoon in our honour – no wonder the poor beast was tough.

After supper we slumped wearily and contentedly around the table, enjoying the last of several of bottles of wine and idly watching geckos making lightning dashes at passing mosquitoes. Two young *Guardia Civil* entered the bar removing their uncomfortable looking tricorns, and proceeded to unsling their rifles.

"You're welcome to sit with us," Antonio invited, and they squeezed in between him and John, placing their revolver belts on the table in front of them. Pedro and Carlos seemed younger than other *guardia* we had seen. Perhaps they were new recruits. Antonio ordered another bottle of wine. The policemen were clearly enjoying this break in their rather lonely existence, and the prospect of spending some time in the company of two young women.

"Who would like a glass of anis?" the older one asked.

"No thanks," Susan shook her head. "I've had plenty of wine."

Andrew, Antonio and John shook their heads.

I should have done the same. I had already had plenty of wine and a very long day in the sun, and the *anis* went straight to my head. After a while the rest of the party returned to the *posada* in search of their beds and only David and I remained. Several glasses of *anis* and an hour later it seemed like a good idea to see if the younger *Guardia Civil*'s pistol, lying on the table in front of me, was really loaded.

"Hey, Pedro, is this loaded? Let me see."

I reached for the gun, quickly took it out of the holster and waved it unsteadily at the window. In my inebriated state I failed to notice the stunned silence around the table and the white face of the owner of the gun.

Carlos grabbed his own gun and pointed it threateningly at me.

"Put it down," he ordered.

Laughing, I took aim – I still hadn't realised that this was no longer funny to anyone except me. Thank god for David who, still reasonably sober, leapt to his feet.

"*No pasa nada*," he calmed them. "It was a joke, there is no problem." Then he turned to me. "Jill, this is serious, put down the gun NOW. Please forgive her, she's not used to the wine and the *anis*."

Carlos reluctantly stopped pointing his pistol at my head and I quickly put Pedro's weapon on the table. I noticed that nobody in the bar was laughing. Through the fog of *anis* it was becoming clear that the policemen's sense of humour failure and my tipsy state had nearly caused an unpleasant, if not fatal, incident.

"Go to the *posada* and do not leave it until tomorrow. If I see you again you will be arrested." The two policemen ordered me out of the bar. I had got off lightly.

With words of warning to David to take me back to the *posada* immediately and keep me under control in the future, they collected hats and rifles and marched angrily out of the bar. We all breathed a sigh of relief and David apologised to Jose, the bar owner, for the incident. He grabbed my arm and frogmarched me back to the *posada*.

"At least you can't do any more damage tonight" he laughed.

I loved him all the more for not reading me the riot act.

"Don't tell Antonio," I begged him. "I would be so embarrassed."

In the dark of the *posada* entrance he leaned me against the wall – probably so that I shouldn't fall over – and kissed me slowly and lovingly.

"What's it worth not to tell him?" he whispered, teasing me with his tongue.

"Anything, I promise," I slurred, as David's face seemed to float unsteadily in front of me. "But you'll have to wait for anything more than a kiss unless you want to get us arrested by those two heavies. Sex is a capital crime and they would probably hang us."

"If you insist," he laughed. "I'll hold you to that."

We stumbled up the stairs and he made sure I was safely inside the bedroom. "Drink lots of water," he advised, "an *anis* hangover is the worst there is."

I slept fitfully, probably due to the combination of sunstroke and *anis*, and as predicted, woke to a cracking headache and a Sahara desert mouth. But it seemed that none of my travelling companions had yet heard of last night's escapade, and I heaved a sigh of relief that I was at least to be spared that embarrassment.

CHAPTER THIRTY-FIVE

Yunquera

As we approached Yunquera, the blue and white roof tiles of the church reflected the late afternoon sun. It had been a long day's ride. Although my hangover had improved somewhat since the morning, my head was still pounding and I definitely wouldn't be sampling the wine for which the town was famous. The village was pretty, with old street lanterns and green and white ceramic guttering on the houses. The usual curious crowd of children and dogs followed us to the *posada* door, to be shooed away by Joaquín, the owner. I remembered a comment from George John Cayley who reported that "the *posada* en Yunquera is a hovel with no beds".

"I hope Cayley was wrong about the *posada*," I said with misgivings as Andrew and I rode through the big wooden doors. But either things had changed or Cayley was mistaken, as the rooms were clean and the stables spacious.

We had passed a small white chapel amongst trees at the entrance to the town, dedicated to the Virgen del Carmen, patron saint of the three Spanish fleets: fishing, merchant, and war.

Antonio told us that it had been built by an eighteenth century emigrant from Yunquera who decided to return from America. A storm threatened to sink his ship, and he prayed to the Virgen del Carmen, the saviour of all sailors, to spare him, and in exchange he would build her a chapel in the mountains. She heard him and he was saved. He kept his promise and built the chapel. The people of Yunquera are very devoted to the saint and when the men leave the village for long periods to work in the olive or wheat harvest they visit the chapel to ask for her blessing. When they return, they make a pilgrimage, accompanied by their families and workmates to the chapel to give thanks to this Virgen del Carmen of the Sierra de las Nieves.

My overriding memory of La Yunquera was seeing *La Majestad*, the host or holy communion being carried down the street. As dusk fell we heard the church bell tolling.

"That's an eerie sound," Susan put her glass down. "Sounds like a funeral bell."

She was right. The *posada* owner beckoned us to the door of the courtyard. When a villager's family had requested the last rites for a dying person the priest and entourage, carrying the sacred host in a large silver container, walked through the village to attend to his spiritual needs. At any hour of the day or night the solemn tolling of the church bells announced the imminent procession from the church. The tolling passing bell was believed to frighten off evil spirits, which are reputed to try to steal the soul at the moment of death. Men removed their hats and women crossed themselves. The children left their games to gawp at the priest in his full robes, as he trod imperiously over the cobbles. From the *posada* we had a front row view of this impressive cortège and the dirge of the bell gave me goosebumps. Along the route to the house of the dying, the silent watchers in their doorways kneeled as the host passed. The village elders carried candles and lanterns to light the way, casting ghostly shadows on the white walls of the narrow cobbled streets. In the silence the choirboy rang his bell – a monotonous, compelling sound – as if he feared he would arrive too late.

Parties and fiestas all stop as the host passes. Unfamiliar with this ceremony, we didn't know whether to kneel or cross ourselves and did some embarrassed shuffling at the *posada* entrance. The invalid's house had been decorated with flowers and religious hangings, and the last we saw of the priest was as he climbed the stairs to impart the last rites with the whole family on their knees.

As soon as the bell ceased, life returned to normal as if there had been no interruption.

It is the custom in Andalucía for all the villagers to support the family of the deceased. In a rural community, funerals are almost always held in the evening, after the day's work is done in the fields. Before refrigeration existed the burial always took place on the day of death, particularly in the summer. At five o'clock the church bell tolled. Then the funeral cortège began, accompanied by melancholy chants. Three stops were made and at each a requiem intoned. During each requiem the coffin was placed on the ground, and the priest made the sign of the cross with holy water and incense. If the deceased was rich, a mourner carried a table covered with a black cloth on which the coffin was placed instead of on the ground. In the north of Spain if a farmer died all his animals would lead the funeral cortège. A sign of wealth was that the religious contingent accompanied the coffin into the cemetery – a poor man's funeral was left by the priest at the cemetery gates. Throughout the procession a family member led the party, intoning the Lord's Prayer and thanking the accompanying villagers with "God will repay you all".

Most Spanish cemeteries, particularly in Andalucía, have niches for the coffins instead of graves. Once the coffin has arrived at the cemetery, the family or pallbearers hoist the coffin into the niche – quite a struggle if the niche is on the third or fourth level and the deceased was a corpulent person.

A bucket of cement and a trowel are then produced and the niche is sealed. The cost of a niche was beyond the means of the less well-off and they were buried in a shallow grave in a part of the cemetery known as *la olla* – the saucepan. They were taken to the cemetery in the parish coffin and dropped into the grave through a hinged base.

The cemetery was known as the land of truth, death being considered the only truth, and life merely an illusion. In some villages it was the custom to leave the deceased in a room with a bell attached to his hand for twenty-four hours. If he revived the movement of the bell would alert the gravediggers that life was still there.

If a mass is to be said it is the custom for the women to enter the church to offer support to the family. The menfolk remain outside to offer their condolences to the men of the deceased's family who stand in a line on the steps looking very uncomfortable in their black suits and ties.

In many Andalucían houses it was the custom to paint all the belongings of the deceased black, and in Seville, during a funeral, the neighbours moved the furniture so that nothing remained to remind the family of the deceased's presence. If a baby belonging to a very poor family died they would save themselves the cost of a funeral by keeping the tiny corpse in alcohol or strong *aguardiente* – rough *anis* – and wait until an adult died. The baby would then be buried in the coffin with the adult.

An American author, Walter Starkie, wrote of a gypsy funeral he witnessed in the caves in Guadix, close to Granada. In the centre of the cave was an open coffin containing the body of a tiny child, with painted cheeks and lips. The body was wrapped in red and blue ribbons and the coffin decorated with flowers and surrounded by candles. Starkie was shocked at what he describes as a "grotesque orgy" of rejoicing, the night spent in singing and dancing, and drinking out of *botas*, wineskins. A flask of *anis* was sprayed over the coffin. An old gypsy told him:

> The child is up there, in heaven, he already has wings sprouting from his little shoulders. Why should his family not jump for joy and shout and dance, the child was lucky to die so early. Have we *calés*, gypsies, so much to be thankful for in life? What a deal of sorrow and suffering that child has escaped.

D'Avillier was also surprised to witness a child's wake, which was enlivened by mourners dancing accompanied by castanets. He was told that all young children join the glorious company of angels round the throne of God immediately they die. Therefore there is rejoicing rather than sorrow. After the dancing finished a joyful peal of church bells sounded through the streets. One gravestone bore the epitaph:

> There is beyond the sky a heaven of joy and love
> And holy children, when they die, go to that world
> above.

***

Supper at the *posada* was rice with fried eggs and tomato sauce called *huevos a la cubana*.

"It can't be *cubana* unless there is a fried banana as well," Susan argued.

But it was a good mixture with or without bananas, somewhat spoilt by a story that David told us just as we were about to eat, about a famous dog called Seven Waters. He was so named because, in an effort to economise, his owner, the *posada* owner, gave the dog the used plates to lick. He said that seven licks of the giant dog's tongue left them cleaner than washing them.

After dinner, the local *Guardia Civil* came to check our papers: probably done to provide an excuse to stay for a free drink. David was giving me the look that said, "no *anis*". He needn't have worried, just the smell of aniseed made me feel nauseous. We sat in the courtyard under the vine and Joaquin's twelve year old niece, Pepa, danced and sang for us.

It was a Quijote-like scene with muleteers, their loads, the *Guardia Civil*, the odd chicken, us, and a couple of mangy cats. Pepa sang of smugglers and bandits, and danced rumbas and *sevillanas*, the typical flamenco dance from Sevilla which all little girls learned as soon as they could walk. The muleteers clapped to the rhythm. The *Guardia Civil* actually smiled, particularly the younger one who only looked about eighteen. A truly magical evening.

One of the muleteers, Juan, a slim, nut-brown man of about thirty, talked to us of his mules, who he obviously adored. His face lit up and creased into a toothless ear-to-ear grin as he recounted their histories.

"My very favourite mule, Castaña, had to be sold. We had no money and we needed to eat," he told us. "I sold her to Pedro, a man in the next village, although it broke my heart to lose her. He took her home to Cártama, about seventeen kilometres away.

"Two nights later, my wife, Maria, shook me awake. 'I hear a mule in the street and somebody is banging on the door. Quick, go and see what the problem is.'"

Juan stumbled down the steep stairs. The knocking on the front door continued. Irritated at the interruption to his sleep he opened the door. His much-loved mule, Castaña, stood there, bleeding from her tightly hobbled forelegs that she had used to knock on the door. She had travelled the seventeen kilometres from her new home with her legs tightly roped together, determined to find Juan and the home she had known all her life. Juan led her through the house into her stall in the patio, where his other mules were calling out to her. He removed the rope hobbles and bathed her wounds. But Pedro, her new owner, came back to fetch her the next day, when Juan was out and only Maria was at home. He wanted the mule he had paid for, but when Castaña heard him she went mad, bucking and kicking and squealing as only an enraged mule can. Pedro finally managed to get hold of her head collar and proceeded up the street dragging his very reluctant purchase behind him.

When we woke in the morning the mule trains had already left and we began the last day of our ride. Across the mountains to Álora.

CHAPTER THIRTY-SIX

Riding Home

"None who has not ridden in Spain can form any correct idea of the general aspect of this wild country, its vast monotonous plains, its wilderness of mountain chains where all is grand in its loneliness and desolation."
– Louisa Tenison

Pitirri and Sebastian brought out the horses and, for the last time, we slung our *alforjas* on to the saddles and set out on the final leg of our journey through Alozaina, towards the village of Álora.

David, on his big grey gelding, rode at the head of the party with Antonio, with the grooms bringing up the rear. The path was rough and I let Krishna have his head as we traversed some terrifying shale hillsides where one slip could send horse and rider spiralling down the yawning precipices. But they were sure-footed and seemed to sense that we were heading for home. We stopped briefly in Alozaina for coffee and in my case for aspirin for the remains of my hangover, which David offered me with a conspiratorial grin. Susan raised her eyebrows but I attributed my malaise to my dose of sunstroke and she seemed to be convinced.

As we descended into the riverbed, dazzling with red and pink oleanders, we heard what seemed like moaning: and it turned out to be a group of muleteers winding their way alongside the other bank of the river, singing monotonous *rondeños* – which have been described by one unappreciative traveller as "wild, barbarous, melancholy howling".

This inspired Pitirri to break into song. We proceeded on our way through the olive grove named the valley of Little Bread, past little white farmhouses, each with a grape vine shading the door and surrounded by prickly pears with their scarlet flowers, whose spiny, wrinkled leaves were likened by George Denis to "ugly deformed old dowagers, bedizened with innumerable jewels".

Lunch was a stop at a little roadside bar. The Spanish omelette with potatoes and onions was delicious, followed by sweet muscatel grapes. A perfect meal for a blindingly hot day.

Later, as the horses climbed wearily up a grassy path towards some cork oaks, Antonio signalled for us all to stop.

"You see across the track there is some barbed wire with a gate? We are about to cross a *dehesa*, a cork oak forest, where fighting bulls are grazing. Keep together and don't speak – they normally won't attack anyone on horseback, so whatever happens don't dismount. If we leave them in peace we'll be fine. I will go first, and Pitirri will close the gate behind us."

We all looked nervously at the field of oak trees, but could see no sign of the beasts. Fighting bulls, depending on their age, can weigh anywhere between three hundred and six hundred kilos.

"Perhaps," I whispered to Susan, "these are young ones."

"Don't count on it," David said. "Pitirri told me that there are seven fully grown bulls who have been separated from the herd as they will be going to the bullfight in Seville next week. They probably weigh more than five hundred kilos each. But relax, we'll be fine."

Wishing I felt as confident, I followed Andrew through the gate. We rode in single file behind Antonio into the grove of trees and glanced around surreptitiously for the sight of a swishing tail or set of horns. However, after a while we relaxed, though Antonio frowned at our nervous whispering.

"Silence."

And then we saw them, perfectly camouflaged in the shade of a giant oak. They were dozing in a dusty hole. Two were sleeping and the remaining five stood, swishing off the flies with their tails. They looked peaceful enough as they blinked at us with sleepy eyes. The horses snorted nervously and John was having trouble controlling Gitano, his black stallion. Krishna and Platero walked past the bulls sideways but otherwise behaved perfectly. I wondered what would happen if Gitano threw John. Would he be able to outrun the bull if it attacked him? I indulged in a pleasant fantasy of unpopular John running for his life pursued by six hundred kilos of angry bull.

Soon we passed through the gate, held open by Sebastian, and into safety.

"Why are there seven bulls?" I asked David. "I thought that a bull fight consisted of six."

"There always has to be a spare, in case one goes lame or gets hurt on the journey," he told me.

Seeing these magnificent animals close up made me realise just how brave the matadors were. I now couldn't wait to see a bullfight and hoped we would be lucky enough to see Antonio Ordoñez perform.

***

Later in the afternoon, within sight of the distant El Hacho, the mountain behind Álora, we stopped to water the horses from a well. A large horizontal wheel was pulled by a donkey walking in circles. As the donkey pulled, the wheel raised buckets of water.

Dusk fell as we rode our tired horses beside the Guadalhorce River with the lights of Álora in the distance and the red glow of the sunset fading over the dusky purple mountains. The hoarse croaking of the frogs from the riverbed was deafening, and the eagles were still cruising over the mountain in search of wandering cats. It felt like more than ten days since we had left the village. David and I lingered behind the others, holding hands under the cover of the fading light.

***

We were home; saddle-sore and tired but, as Théophile Gautier put it, 'the pleasure of travelling consists in the obstacles, the fatigue and even the danger'.

We had met with no danger, and there had not been a bandit in sight, but I had achieved my ambition and experienced the same obstacles and fatigue as those early travellers. I had lived my adventure.

As an added bonus David and I had some days together to look forward to.

Once again the village turned out to see us. Antonio's little dog Chico danced around his master's horse, overjoyed to see him, and Juana stood beaming in the doorway.

The horses seemed to heave a sigh of relief as they were led into their own stables. Although we would ride out the next day for a farewell picnic, most of their hard work was done. Our saddlebags full of filthy clothes were spirited away by Carmen, Juana's assistant, and we all fell into a welcome shower, emptied through a hole in the roof by Juan, the kitchen hand, always mindful of the scarcity of water. A bottle of chilled red wine stood ready in the patio alongside a bottle of lemonade, the components of a refreshing *tinto de verano*, summer red wine. A delicious soup of chicken and vegetables followed by a salad revived us all and even John was relaxed and happy.

Later, as we sat round the table, enjoying the cool breeze, Antonio, with Chico ensconced on his lap, asked if we had heard the story of the white wolf.

"Tell us," I said.

"Well – once upon time, a very long time ago, a wolf roamed the mountains a little to the north of here. This was nothing special about this wolf except for the fact that he was completely white. He was found by sheepdogs and, instead of killing the cub, which would have been normal, they stood around him, startled by the colour of the abandoned animal. He looked like a wolf and he smelled like a wolf but he was as white as a lamb and was not travelling with the wolf packs that roamed the mountains.

"The surprised shepherd took him to the village and put him with a sheep that was suckling her lambs. The hungry cub began to feed as if with his own mother. Time passed and the wolf cub grew amongst the herd and went with them to graze in the mountains. In moments of danger he hid amongst the sheep whilst the big dogs defended the flock from predators. When he was fully grown, his fur was still white and his eyes were scary. The village dogs used to pick on him and his white fur was often stained with blood.

"Little by little, he distanced himself from the herd and stopped going into the village. All the villagers recognised his howls and at night they were not afraid. The shepherd was so attached to him that every day he took him food, and he never attacked the sheep. He was just a wandering orphan who found solace in the company of the shepherd and his dogs, who were the only ones who treated him well. The man and the wolf were inseparable until the day when bandits attacked the shepherd. When he resisted, they killed the dogs and began to beat him to death. Suddenly the bandits' horses snorted and whinnied as if there was some danger. The bandits paused in their attack on the shepherd, and suddenly an enormous white wolf launched himself at the throat of one of the men. After tearing his throat out, he went for a second bandit and the rest tried to flee from the white devil, but their horses had bolted in fear and on foot the men were no match for the avenging wolf.

"As he lay dying, the shepherd told the story of how the wolf had defended him, and the villagers found the bodies of seven bandits, all with the tooth marks of the wolf on their necks. The wolf was never seen again, but the villagers heard his howling for many years after."

We were silent after Antonio finished his story. He looked tired and his air of melancholy seemed to have returned now that we were back in Álora. Why, I wondered, had Vicki, his girlfriend, ended her life jumping from the cliffs of El Chorro. And why had she taken her dog to its death with her?

CHAPTER THIRTY-SEVEN

The Picnic

We all slept late, rejoicing in the comfortable beds and pillows.

"Do you think we can beat the men to the shower?" Susan stretched luxuriously. "I can smell coffee and perhaps there's some cow's milk. I'm really fed up with the taste of goat. I'll call you when I'm finished in the bathroom."

She grabbed her towel and disappeared in search of Juan to bring water.

I lay enjoying the cool morning breeze which gently moved the thin curtains. I had dreamed of big black bulls and somewhere in my dream Nanny Elsie and Vicente were chasing something or were they being chased? Hard as I tried, I couldn't remember. My mother used to say that if you could remember a dream it would come true.

My thoughts turned to Vicente. I hoped that David and I would not be seen on our way through Málaga, en route for Granada. Whilst Vicente was very attractive, and it would be nice to keep him in reserve, it was David who I loved and who had turned my world upside down.

"I've been calling you," Susan, her hair wrapped in a towel, opened the door. "If you lie there dreaming you'll never get a shower. Thank goodness Juana and Carmen have managed to get some of our clothes washed – I have nothing left to wear. What are you dreaming about anyway?" she asked, as I pushed back the sheet and got out of bed.

"Have you nicked the shampoo?" I rummaged in my rucksack.

"No, I haven't – and you haven't answered my question. Who or what are you dreaming about?"

"David, of course. He's really got under my skin and I can't wait to spend some time together. It's sort of a secret, but we're going to spend a few days together in Granada."

"That's great, I'm so glad for you." She hugged me spontaneously. "He's really sexy. Not my type, as you know, but I can see the attraction. How are you getting back to the UK?"

"I'm booked on the ship HMS Orantes. She's due in Gibraltar in a few days' time. It sounds very grand but actually my berth is on H deck, and I have to share with five other people. My cabin's well below decks I think, but it's quite cheap when you consider all your food is free on board."

"What a great way to end the holiday. I don't want to go home."

I wondered how Susan was going to solve her situation with her fiancé and her attraction for Tomás. Perhaps even she didn't know, as she just looked thoughtful.

"See you for coffee." I left her to her thoughts. She would no doubt tell me in her own time.

We were looking forward to a relaxing day ahead of us. Antonio had planned a picnic by the river, and we all wanted to buy postcards and small presents to take home.

At midday we congregated in the stables and helped Juana fill our saddlebags with food, drink, rugs to spread on the ground, and our swimming costumes. The horses all wore head collars under their bridles so that we could tether them while we relaxed. David brought his drawing pad and pens, to record this last day of our journey.

We left the village and turned south down towards the station and the Guadalhorce River. Although there was little water in the main river, after a ride of half an hour Pitirri led us to a smaller stream above Pizarra. Here there were grassy banks under shady poplar trees and deep pools in the sandy riverbed.

Dismounting, and tethering his horse to a tree, Antonio said, "If you want to swim with your horse, get Sebastian or Pitirri to take the saddle off for you, but I suggest you leave the bridle on or you may find it difficult to control them. Particularly Gitano," he told John. "He's a bit nervous in the water."

Having shed riding clothes and boots and changed into swimsuits we had a lot of trouble getting onto the horses without the aid of stirrups but after some inelegant scrabbling Susan, Andrew and I were mounted. John had decided to wait and see how we fared.

It is said that Arab horses don't like water, but after some initial nervousness Susan and I persuaded Krishna and Platero to venture into the first deep pool, and Ligero, with Andrew on board, didn't want to be left behind. Riding bareback on a swimming horse is a difficult feat when the coat is wet and slippery. Chico swam around in circles barking with excitement, and soon David joined us in the water. I was enjoying the sight of his muscled, suntanned body when disaster struck Susan – Platero took fright and skewed sideways, and off she went into the water, losing her hold on the wet reins. The startled animal galloped out onto the bank, shook himself and took off up the riverbed in the direction of home with Pitirri and Sebastian in hot pursuit. The rest of the party were doubled up with laughter.

"It's a long walk home," David joked.

"I'm sure Pitirri will catch him," Antonio laughingly reassured her. "But he will probably go all the way home to Álora."

"I'm so sorry, Antonio, I should have kept hold of him," Susan apologised when the laughter subsided.

"It's not a problem, they'll find him, and it's not as if there is a lot of traffic on the road."

Antonio lay back in the shade and closed his eyes, with a damp Chico beside him. John decided to swim without his horse, which he tethered to the poplar tree, and found a deep clear pool below a large smooth rock which was ideal for diving. David opened a bottle of white wine, placed a water melon to chill in the river and we all settled down to an idyllic afternoon of swimming, eating and drinking.

It was two hours later when a hot and dusty Pitirri and Sebastian returned. The fugitive had been found but he had lost a shoe in his wild dash up the riverbed. They had left him back in Álora and brought another horse for Susan.

David sat a little way up the bank happily sketching. I dozed in the shade to the noise of hundreds of crickets. A kingfisher darted past, and an army of little terrapins plodded up the sandbanks and plopped into the pools.

In the cool of the early evening, we finished the wine that we had kept chilled in one of the pools. Pitirri and Sebastian saddled up and we all headed for home.

I didn't want this holiday to end. I wanted it to start all over again. But they say "you must never go back". The future and another adventure with David would start tomorrow. All that mattered was that we would be together.

For our last supper Juana had surpassed herself: apart from the usual *gazpacho* she had prepared a delicious dish of rice with partridges. Carmen had returned our clothes washed and ironed. We were all ready to pack for our departure on the next morning's train to Málaga. John, Andrew, and Susan were heading for the airport to return to the UK. David and I were to catch the bus from Málaga to Granada.

CHAPTER THIRTY-EIGHT

Alone At Last

"Love is like the wind, you can't see it but you can feel it." – Nicholas Sparks

In the morning we said a sad farewell to Pitirri, Sebastian and our horses. Krishna had behaved impeccably and carried me safely over many dangerous places, and I would miss him. He snuffled as I gave him my last polo and I whispered in his ear that I would be back. Susan had also been saying farewell to her horse, and appeared, kicking angrily at a dung beetle.

"Hey, what did that beetle ever do to you. What's the problem?"

"Oh, I'm just cheesed off at Tomás. I know it's a long way, but he promised to come."

"Perhaps he'll be at the station. But if he has to come all the way on that old donkey he'll never make it. You know it's difficult for him," I consoled her.

"Yeah, I know. But there's no harm in wishing, is there." She brightened up. "Anyway, I'm planning to come back in October and he should have less work then. We'll be able to spend more time together."

"Does that mean you're cancelling your wedding plans?"

"Yes, I think so. If nothing else I think I've realised that I really don't love Paul. Or not enough to get married anyway. But I'm not sure whether Tomás is serious or not, and it's not easy as we have to talk in sign language. I think I'll just have to wait and see what happens."

"Write and tell me?"

Antonio was calling us.

"You're going to miss the train. We need to hurry."

Juana and Carmen kissed us and bid us Godspeed.

"*Buen viaje* – have a good journey, and come back soon."

Our cases and rucksacks would be taken to the station in Antonio's antique car, one of only two in the village, and we walked with Chico down the hill.

For once, the train was early and we had to run the last few yards as it steamed noisily into the little station. We hardly had time to say goodbye to Antonio before the station master blew his whistle and we scrambled on board.

There were few seats and the carriages were hot and smelly. We rumbled past the hedges of spiky aloes and prickly pears alongside the almost dry riverbed. Andrew and John stood in the corridor discussing the birds we had seen while Susan, David and I exchanged addresses and phone numbers. The carriage was full of families heading to Málaga and, as usual, the floor was littered with the remains of bread and melon skins. Only a short time to go until David and I could be alone and open about our feelings.

The train grunted its way into Málaga station and, after hugs and goodbyes, we left the others to make their way by bus to the airport.

"Call me as soon as you get to England," Susan called back.

"I promise."

Shouldering our rucksacks, David and I headed towards the city centre. At last we could hold hands, though any greater show of affection in the street would be frowned upon.

"We'd better find a cheap shop and buy a ring for appearance's sake, Mrs Smith," grinned David.

I gazed at him in surprise that such deceit was necessary. But I realised that he was serious.

"Hang on here, look after the back packs and I'll see if I can find a wedding ring."

I glanced around nervously, afraid that Vicente or his friends might be in Málaga and see me with David. I had promised Vicente that I would return to see him in ten days and here I was, checking into a hostel with another man, wearing a wedding ring.

David returned with what looked like a curtain ring. "I hope it fits you, Mrs Smith." He slipped it on my finger.

"Perfect. So long as I don't have to promise to obey you, husband."

"Non-negotiable. You will do as you're told."

"That sounds promising." I squeezed his hand. "Let's find somewhere to stay."

We found a run-down hostel close to the bus station. Only an inside room was available.

The tiny room was stifling, its window opening onto a communal passageway. The furniture was sparse. A broken chair, a small round table and above the bed a picture of a saint being attacked by enormous dogs. The iron bedstead looked as if it would creak loudly. We dropped our rucksacks. My heart thudded as I reached out to touch him nervously, like a rabbit caught in the headlights. Suddenly I didn't know what to do. Our lips met. I ran my hands through his hair, and his work-roughened hands caressed me. I had watched his hands for so many days, playing the guitar, or calming a restless horse, and now it was my turn to be stroked. I began to relax. I closed my eyes. Gently David pushed me down on the bed. I drew him down to me. I wanted this to be perfect, but the nervous anticipation of this long-awaited moment and the heat in the tiny airless room meant that I was soaked in sweat.

"David," I whispered.

"Mmmm," he said, pulling me closer

"We both smell of horses."

He pulled away and looked at me in disbelief.

"Well, we'd better fix that," he laughed.

Grabbing towels he propelled me along the corridor to the shower room. It was tiny and by the time we had removed each other's riding boots, jeans and shirts we were helpless with laughter and the awkwardness of the moment was over. Behind the gruesome shower curtain, under the feeble flow of cold water, we made slippery, soapy love. A loud banging on the door shattered the moment.

"Enough, haven't you finished yet?"

Glowing from love and embarrassment, and wearing a very skimpy towel, I crept past the portly guest who, shampoo in hand, had being queuing patiently. We collapsed on the rickety bed, laughing and loving in a rough mass of damp tangled sheets.

Later that day, we came up for air and strolled out into the busy city streets in search of a cool drink. The heat rose up from the pavements and there was not a breath of wind. In the early hours we finally slept and in the morning the heat had melted the red and green stripe in my toothpaste.

CHAPTER
THIRTY-NINE

The Road to Granada

"The bus departure is far more like a family gathering than something on a schedule. The passengers, their lives and wishes are more important than the bus, itself more like a dusty animal than a machine."
– V.S. Pritchett on Spanish buses

The bus to Granada left early and we only had time for a quick *churros y chocolate* before boarding. It looked unlikely to make the hundred kilometre trip to Granada in one piece. We all piled in with baskets, bundles, and rucksacks and left the bus station in the centre of Málaga only half an hour late.

The published journey time was four hours, through the mountains behind Málaga, Colmenar, Loja, Santa Fe and Granada. Passing by the cathedral we began to climb, past the Church of our Lady of Victory, Nuestra Señora de la Victoria, built on the site where the Catholic monarchs pitched their tents during the siege of Málaga in 1487.

The air was still and the city was shrouded in morning mist as the sun rose in an orange ball behind the distant range of the Sierra Nevada, promising a scorching day. The driver had trouble with the gears as we crawled up the narrow potholed road, with its sheer drops and blind hairpin bends. Almonds, olives and aloes covered the arid hillsides and herds of goats grazed on what little grass they could find, sometimes climbing up the lower branches of the olive trees to reach a succulent morsel.

After an hour and a half we reached the Puerto del Léon, the Pass of the Lion, and the road became a little less precipitous. The passengers dozed, the women fluttered their fans, and the red plastic seats stuck clammily to thin summer dresses. Loja came and went with its two churches, one a Moorish mosque and the other a sixteenth century Christian church. The town served as a filter for armies advancing up the river to attack Granada and Queen Isabella referred to it as the 'rose between thorns' i.e. the Christian town between Moslem settlements.

Later, we passed the large estates gifted to the Duke of Wellington by a grateful Spanish people as a reward for driving Napoleon out of Spain during the Spanish War of Independence.

"That's where Federico Garcia Lorca was born." David pointed out the sign to the village of Fuente Vaqueros.

"He's one of those authors I have heard of, but never seen any of his books."

"As a young writer, his first play about the impossible love between a butterfly and a cockroach, was not well received. He was jeered at and humiliated."

"I'm not surprised. It doesn't sound very entertaining," I laughed.

"I agree. In Madrid he struck up a friendship with Salvador Dali and Luis Buñuel. However, his friendship with Dali ended and he became depressed and tormented by his homosexuality.

"That may explain his fascination with impossible love," I jibbed.

"One of his best-known poems was written on the death of his great friend, the bullfighter Ignacio Sánchez Mejias, who bled to death after being gored in the bullring. His lament spoke of love, pride, passion and death, It's one of my favourite Spanish poems," David said:

> At five in the afternoon,
> tell the moon to come,
> for I do not want to see the blood
> of Ignacio on the sand.

"What happened to Lorca?"

"Well, when the civil war broke out his friends warned him to leave Spain. He was well known as an intellectual and that alone made him a target for the nationalist regime of General Franco. His left wing reputation and homosexuality probably signed his death warrant, although he always said he hated politics and that he was only on the side of the poor."

"Was he caught?"

"Unfortunately so, and he was denounced for having publicly criticized fascism and defended the Republic."

"What did they do to him?"

"Along with a one-legged school teacher and two bullfighters, Lorca was taken out of the town to the village of Viznar, where he was forced to dig his own grave. The exact spot has never been found.

"Salvador Dali recounted that Lorca was obsessed with his own death and that 'he alluded to it at least five times a day'. He had a bizarre habit of play-acting his own death and insisted that his friends should join in his 'funeral procession'. In a poem he instructed that when he was dead the balcony window should be left open. He even foretold his own death, and that's really weird. He wrote:

> Then I realized I had been murdered.
> They looked for me in cafes, cemeteries and churches...
> But they did not find me.
> They never found me?
> No. They never found me.

"I'll have to read some of his writings – I hope I can find them in London."

Only eleven kilometres from Granada we entered the village of Santa Fe. Situated on the banks of the River Genil, its cobbled streets and imposing stone archways were reminders of the siege of Granada by the Queen Isabella and King Fernando in 1491. Their tented encampment was destroyed by fire after a candle in Isabella's tent was knocked over during the night. The town was built to enable them to continue the siege, and to show the defenders that they had no intention of abandoning their sworn intent to take the city.

For several years before the siege of Granada, Fernando had carried out a systematic destruction of the area around the city, resulting in total devastation of irrigation systems, farms and crops. He had signed a deal with Boabdil – that when the time was right the city would be handed over by him to the Christians. But Boabdil dragged his feet and it was decided to lay siege to the city to speed up the process. No artillery was used as in other sieges since the Christians had no wish to destroy the priceless buildings and cause great loss of life on both sides. It being a city with a large population, they believed it would be easy to starve the inhabitants.

Isabella was reported to be 'the life and soul' of the siege, having brought her children and numerous members of her court to witness the fall of Granada. Here, in the same year, Christopher Columbus received the royal mandate for his voyage in search of America, causing Santa Fe to be known as 'the cradle of America'. He wanted to sail west around the world and had sought support first in Portugal, but had been refused.

Based on writings in the Old Testament stating that the world was six parts earth to one part sea, he reasoned that to sail from Spain westwards to India should be easy. Finally, playing on her fanatic Catholicism, he convinced Queen Isabella that all the savages in the lands where the Spanish flag could be raised would be future converts. It is also rumoured that he convinced Queen Isabella to have an affair with him. Whatever the reason, he received royal funding and in 1492 the ships Santa Maria, Pinta and La Niña sailed from Spain, making their first landfall in the Bahamas.

***

Moslem Granada was a great city with a wealth of art, architecture, and pottery. The Moors built many of the irrigation systems which are still used today and which, particularly in the valleys close to Granada, made the land flourish. Agriculture bloomed with the introduction of rice, sugar cane, dates, and strawberries. The cultivation of mulberry trees and breeding of silkworms also gave rise to an important industry.

After eight centuries of occupation where did they all go when the Christians reconquered Spain – not only the Moors, but also later the many thousands of *moriscos* and Jews? They dispersed and disappeared silently.

Federico García Lorca had this to say about the eviction of the Jews from Granada:

> A disastrous event, an admirable civilization and a poetry, architecture and delicacy unique in the world, were all lost to give way to an impoverished, cowed town, a wasteland populated by the worst bourgeoisie in Spain today.

I hoped that his opinion of Granada was wrong – poisoned by the years of harassment of the Jews, and his own persecution and imprisonment in the city. Granada was the fabled city where the cross had replaced the crescent and Spain was once again under Christian rule.

CHAPTER FORTY

Granada

"Granada shone like a silver vase, set with emeralds and precious stones. It reflected the beauty of a terrestrial paradise." – Washington Irving

It was more than four hours after our departure from Málaga when we caught sight of the mountains behind Granada, the Sierra Nevada, and the pink walls of the Alhambra Palace towering over the legendary city. The walls, which once protected the fortress, straggle haphazardly up the hill, alongside impenetrable hedges of prickly pear cactus. But weary from the bone-rattling ride and stifling heat, all I could think of was a shower and a cold drink. Granada and its wonders would have to wait.

We found a small *pension* in the centre of town close to the bus station, and paid the suspicious old lady at the desk, who asked why our passports showed different names if we were married. I waved my finger with my new wedding ring, which, as David pointed out, should have been on the right hand in Spain.

"We've only just got married and in our country you don't need to change your name."

She looked doubtful but we made good our escape upstairs and collapsed onto another creaky bed, smothering our laughter and hoping she didn't call in the *Guardia Civil* to have us arrested for fornication. The bathroom was on the floor above, but the shower worked and the water was ice cold. Revived, we crept past the witch's cubby hole and went in search of the cheapest restaurant we could find for lunch.

I ordered one of the most economical dishes on the menu, *Tortilla Sacromonte*, advertised as a house speciality. To my horror it turned out to be a mixture of eggs, red peppers and fried brains. My stomach heaved and there was no way I could even look at the blue veined gelatinous lumps lurking in the leathery egg mixture. It reminded me of Nanny Elsie and the gristly sausages. I had a complete sense of humour failure, and we had our first row. I made do with bread, and sulkily and childishly refused David's offer to share his plate of crispy fried anchovies.

David persevered in his attempt to cheer me up and my good humour was soon restored by a delicious ice cream from a street vendor. We walked alongside the River Darro – which in the August afternoon heat was just as foul-smelling as the River Guadalhorce had been in Málaga – and began the climb up the hill to the Alhambra. Little shops selling guitars and souvenirs lined the steep street and the sound of what seemed to be a dancing lesson with stamping feet and clicking castanets drifted from a small window on the building above the guitar shop.

As we climbed, leaving the city centre below us, giant trees shaded the road and water cascaded down irrigation channels on either side, cooling the air. We checked out the Alhambra Palace Hotel, built in 1910 in Moorish style and painted in the same hue of dusky rose as the Alhambra itself. The view from the terrace of the snow-capped Sierra Nevada was stunning. We did not stay long since the cost of a drink was beyond our budget and we still had a long climb to the Alhambra Palace itself and the gardens of the Generalife.

Granada's turbulent history was partly due to its position. Situated at the foot of the Sierra Nevada, traversed by two rivers, the Darro and the Genil, surrounded by fertile valleys, and on the main route from the Mediterranean to the centre of the country, it changed hands between a succession of invading or retreating armies. Mohammed ben Alahmar, founder of the kingdom of Granada, carried out much of the building in the city, and the bulk of the surviving buildings that comprise the Alhambra were completed by Abdul Hachach Yusuf I and his son Mohammed V in the mid-fourteenth century, in the last days of the Nasrid kingdom. Underneath the palace giant water tanks were installed, fed by the River Darro, to supply the Alcázar in case of siege.

It was a small kingdom with a glittering court, and had an abundant water supply and well established commerce. The legal system functioned well, and peace reigned for a while. Literature, learning and the sciences flourished.

A Moorish legend recounts that when Allah created the earth he granted each region five wishes. The requests from Al Andalus were that they should have ripe fruit, a clear blue sky, beautiful women, a sea full of fish, and, finally, good government. Allah refused the last request because this would have created heaven on earth.

The Moors were always a thorn in the Christians' side – they were another race, the invaders, and a nation without a country to be exterminated. United armies swept south and finally, between 1482 and 1492, despite their financial difficulties, Fernando and Isabella succeeded in pushing the Moors back to the Mediterranean coast. Malaga itself fell in 1487 and thousands of Moors fled to Morocco, settling in a town they named Chechouen, in the Rif mountains.

Granada was the last stronghold to fall. After a long siege, secret negotiations and disagreements, Boabdil 'the small', the last Moorish king, surrendered to King Fernando and Queen Isabella, in 1492. The Treaty of Granada was signed whereby the Moors gave up the city and fortresses. They complied with their part of the bargain, and for their part the Christian monarchs agreed the following conditions:

> The Moors were to keep their homes and assets. They would be free to trade and no more taxes would be imposed than those laid down by Moorish law. The mosques would be respected and the muezzins, church officials, would be free to call the faithful to prayer from the minarets. Their customs would be upheld, and no Christians could enter the mosques

without permission of the mosque elders. Justice was to be administered to Moors by Moorish judges, and if the case was between a Moor and a Christian two judges would be assigned. The Koran was still to be taught in the public schools, and mixed marriages would be respected as would true conversions to the Moorish faith. The Jews in Granada and the Alpujarras would have the same rights as the Moors. All prisoners would be exchanged. The irrigation channels would be kept clean and nobody could wash in them or pollute them with rubbish.

As a sign of respect to the Moors, the Christian monarchs walked into the Alhambra to accept the surrender wearing Moorish clothes. However, in their impatience to enter the city the Christian monarchs signed the agreement with no intention of keeping their side of the deal. Their objective was to unify Spain and effect racial and religious integration.

As Boabdil left Granada he is said to have reined in his horse in a mountain pass and turned to take a last tearful look at the city.

His unsympathetic mother jeered at him, 'Will you cry like a woman for a city that you could not defend like a man?'

The mountain pass is still called the Moor's Last Sigh. He was banished to the mountain range behind Granada known as the *Alpujarras* where he spent his time hunting. However, Queen Isabella was warned by her religious advisers that it was an offence to keep faith with infidels and he was eventually banished to Africa.

Boabdil was blamed by many of his former supporters for the loss of Granada as it was deemed a punishment for his unnecessary cruelty towards the Abencerrages. They were a family who had displeased him by supporting his beautiful stepmother, Zoraya – Star of the Morning, in her children's claim for the throne of Granada. Feigning reconciliation, he invited them to the Alhambra palace and, one by one, decapitated them. Some were saved by a young page who risked his life to warn them of the fate of their brethren. It was believed that this bloody revenge brought bad luck on the city and caused the victory of the Catholic kings. In the Patio of the Lions is a fountain which, it is said, has bloodstains of the slaughtered Abencerrages. At night low murmurings are heard as the spirits of the dead converse. Science scoffs at this explanation and says it is the flow of water under the hill on which the Alhambra is built. But popular belief prefers the more romantic version. As William Edward Baxter concludes:

> When science from creation's face
> Enchantment's veil withdraws
> What lovely visions then give place
> To cold material laws.

There were few tourists in the heat of the August afternoon and we were able to wander, hand in hand (since we were now reputedly married) through the splendidly ornate rooms and patios with intricate mosaics and tinkling fountains. The glassless windows were so angled as to keep out the relentless sun and the rooms were cool and airy. I breathed a sigh of contentment. David put his hands on my shoulders, drew me close and kissed me. When he released me, he was smiling. "I assume that sigh was happiness?" he asked.

"It's perfect. Everything's just perfect."

"I seem to remember that you were escaping from boring men. Does that mean I've come up to your expectations?"

"Don't get too complacent," I laughed.

***

He took my hand. We crossed the Hall of the Abencerrajes, who were so foully murdered by Boabdil; the Court of the Myrtles, fragrant with its impeccable hedges; the Court of the Pond; and the Court of the Lions with the white animals representing strength but not exactly a lion since Moslems may not carve or paint an exact representation of any living being.

"Just imagine what it was like when the Moors were here," David ran his hand down a broken piece of wood. "Before the looters and the tourists broke off pieces of this priceless palace. There were

227

schools and mosques – it was just like a small city encircled by the walls. Did you know that they even had special hospitals for lepers and advanced treatments for war wounds? Even Richard Ford renovated a suite of rooms for himself here, and stole many priceless items from the palace."

Sadly the Alhambra was allowed to deteriorate after the departure of the Moors and it was not until the early nineteenth century that work began to repair the damage and neglect of centuries.

During the French occupation of Spain, French soldiers worked on repairs to the abandoned palace, which had become home to smugglers and thieves. However, when Napoleon was defeated in the early 1800s, he gave orders for the Alhambra to be destroyed. But for the bravery of one of his soldiers who defused the explosives, this wonderful palace would have been lost for ever.

In 1812, Wellington imported hundreds of elms from England which now form a dense wood around the Generalife Gardens. Myrtles, roses, oranges and the sound of water fill these romantic gardens and on a summer night the air is alive with the song of nightingales. Alexandre Dumas gushed, 'Nowhere in the world will you find in such a small expanse such fragrance, such freshness, such a multitude of windows, each opening on a corner of paradise.' As we walked through the cool gardens, David told me some of the legends and stories of the palace.

Washington Irving was invited to stay in the derelict and crumbling rooms of the Alhambra itself by the Governor. It was here that he wrote *Tales of the Alhambra* in 1850, recounting many of the legends of Christians and Moors, murders, intrigues and romances of the Muslim dynasties, as told to him by the aged custodian.

He relates the story of an invalid soldier whose job it was to show the infrequent visitors around the palace. One night the soldier heard voices and on entering one of the Court rooms he saw four richly dressed Moors, wearing jewel-encrusted cloaks, in earnest conversation. They beckoned to him, attempting to show him something under the marble floors. But, terrified of the Moorish ghosts he took to his heels, never again to enter the Alhambra. He had heard the legend of the buried Moorish treasure but his fear overcame his greed. His replacement was obviously made of sterner stuff. Ghosts would not deter him if there was treasure to be found. Within a week of commencing his job he had found the treasure, abandoned his employment, bought a house and carriage in Málaga, and lived there in comfort for the rest of his days.

From the gardens of the Generalife we looked out over the river towards the caves of Sacromonte, or sacred mountain. This, David told me, was where the famous gypsies lived and danced for tourists.

We headed off down the hill back into the city for a much-needed glass of wine before visiting the caves.

CHAPTER FORTY-ONE

Maria the Gypsy Queen

"Gypsies were born to be thieves, their parents were thieves, they are brought up with thieves, study to be thieves and finally become thieves and their desire to steal only finishes with death." – Cervantes

"The Gypsy matriarch, Maria La Canastera, is a great friend of mine," Antonio had told us, before we left Álora. "Tell her you are friends of mine and she will look after you."

Crossing the River Darro once again we wound our way through the narrow streets of the Albaicín heading for the Plaza Nueva and the Sacromonte district. The caves there have been used over the centuries by fugitives from justice, deserters from the many armed conflicts, the *moriscos* after the rebellion in 1569, and finally by the gypsies.

The majority of historians now agree that the first gypsies arrived in Spain from the Punjab. Romani, their language, is more similar to Sanskrit than to any other language. However, the word gypsy is said to mean "Egyptian" (in Spanish 'Gitano' – 'Egiptano') and some of them did arrive in Spain through Gibraltar from Egypt. Many authors describe them as 'children of Egypt'. It is said that when the Virgin Mary and her child fled to Egypt, the gypsies refused them food and shelter. God, in his anger, condemned all gypsies to seven years of wandering before they were allowed to settle down.

When groups arrived in France from the East in the fifteenth century they were received with loathing. The men were hanged or sent to the galleys and the women scourged or mutilated. George Borrow (the evangelical bible-seller and gypsiologist) spent time among the gypsies in Granada and wrote in *The Zincali*, 'They arrived like flights of wasps and led a miserable existence since Granada is the poorest town in Spain.'

Many of them arrived with the Christian armies in 1490 and were initially tolerated. However, when the Jews were evicted (or converted) the gypsies' failure to integrate, settle down or subscribe to the Catholic faith made them a target for Queen Isabella's zeal. A series of new rules were applied to them: they were not allowed to travel in groups, own property, or be blacksmiths, and had to convert to Christianity. Over the next two hundred years new penalties – whipping, amputation of ears, and even slavery – were applied to their perceived misdoings and failure to conform. In 1749 around twelve thousand gypsies from Granada were jailed or sent to forced labour.

They were accused of pagan rites, witchcraft, exploiting and kidnapping children, and vagrancy. They were feared and hated. Legend accuses them of making the nails which were used to nail Christ to the cross, or that, on the contrary, they stole the nails from his hands which removed his pain.

One of the few to support the gypsies was the poet Federico García Lorca, who describes them as 'the most elemental, deep and aristocratic of my country and who keep the fire, the blood and the alphabet of universal Andaluz truth'.

Hans Christian Anderson in 1860 recounted that his coach ride was made:

> more tolerable by the charms of nut-brown gypsy nymphets very different from the pale, flaxen haired maidens he was used to and he saw "a girl of about twelve, fully developed, a real Murillo beauty...

scantily dressed, doubtless because of the terrific
heat. She had a juicy bunch of grapes in her hand…
we were indeed in a hot country.

Some of the favourite gypsy curses are, "God grant that you may
fall into the hands of an executioner and be dragged as an adder to
death" or "mayest thou famish of hunger and may dogs devour thee".

As we approached the Sacromonte area the sun was setting, the
strains of a lone guitar filled the evening air and we could see the
entrances to the caves, each brilliantly whitewashed and surrounded
with aloes and prickly pear plants. Hobbled donkeys and mules
nibbled on brown grass and rubbish and naked children shrieked
and played in the dust. David asked the way to Maria's cave and
there she was, arms folded over her ample bosom, majestic in the
doorway of her domain. The mention of Antonio's name sent her
into rhapsodies of praise for him, such a gentleman, so good looking,
so charming, and a *muy buen amigo*. She embraced us both and led
us into the cave.

From D'Avilliers' description of 'dens full of children, stark
naked, black as little negroes, crawling about in the midst of
famishing poultry and filthy domestic pigs', I had imagined a dark and
rather squalid dwelling, but this was far from the truth. It consisted
of two rooms, the back room was used as a bedroom, where Maria,
her husband and her children slept. It was rather cramped but just
enough room for four. A small alcove served as a kitchen, with a
hole in the roof to let out the cooking smoke. The main room served
as a living room and, with chairs placed around the sides and the
earth floor well swept, the scenario for the dancing. It was spotless
and every inch of whitewashed wall was covered with photographs
of celebrities who had visited the cave. Enrique, Maria's husband, as
skinny as she was buxom, sat on a small wooden chair at the cave's
entrance, guitar in hand, preparing for the night's entertainment,
whilst the dark-skinned children continued to play. I was enthralled.
I had imagined dirt, robbers, and a tourist trap. Instead I had found
this enchanting family, and a warm welcome and to use Borrow's
words, 'copper-coloured gypsies with blue-black hair'.

"Maria," she called out to her small daughter. "Get dressed, it's time to dance."

The child disappeared into the back of the cave and reappeared wearing a threadbare flounced dress, several layers of dirt on her face and hands, and red dancing shoes several sizes too big for her. A group of tourists had arrived and Maria sent Enrique, the youngest boy, to call the other dancers. Glasses of sweet wine were handed round and we took our seats.

"Antonio told me Maria and her family are famous for the *zambra* dance," David whispered.

"This is the pure form of flamenco," Enrique said

"You may know that King Fernando and Queen Isabella forbade the performance of Moorish dances, so our ancestors modified the Zambra into a type of dance which was acceptable to their rulers."

The music began and we spent an enchanting hour listening to Enrique and a cousin, Eduardo, playing for the dancers who entertained us with *sevillanas*, *zambras*, and *tangos*. Big Maria, despite her size, moved with grace, although she looked older than her forty-seven years. Little Maria stole everyone's hearts as she twirled and stamped her way through a Rumba, twisting and thrusting her bony little hips and tossing her head like the adults. Her dark eyes flashed and she pouted, her face seeming old before its time. Little Enrique, who wasn't more than four years old, put in a brief appearance on the dance floor. In his polka-dot shirt, tied at the waist, tight trousers and high-heeled boots he was the star act. I had read Karel Capek's description of flamenco:

> Take a highland fling, a cakewalk, a tango, a Cossack gopak, an Apache dance, a fit of frenzy, unconcealed lechery and other frantic movements, kindle them to a white heat and begin to batter them with castanets, shouting all the while.

To the contrary, I found it exciting and fascinating with its Moorish undertones. I was delighted to find I totally disagreed with him and was fascinated by the elegance and romance of the dancers.

233

As the tourists left, Maria took my arm. "Stay a while," she said to David, "let's sit outside in the cool."

We carried chairs to the door of the cave and sat enjoying the wine and the cool breeze. Maria told us how her father had been a basket maker, but she became so famous as a *zambra* dancer that she danced for King Alfonso XIII.

"I am glad that some of my children are following in my footsteps, it's probably the only way they'll make any money," she sighed.

The only professions open to gypsies were as horse traders, shearers, basket makers, charcoal burners, musicians, or dancers.

"There's still a lot of prejudice, and the children don't want to go to school because the other children gang up on them."

All around us the women were lighting the cooking fires, which were deterring the hordes of mosquitoes which had instantly spotted our Anglo-Saxon skin. We talked about Antonio and told her about our ride to Ronda. Enrique joined us – a quiet, gentle man, very different from his exuberant wife.

When we finally got up to leave, Maria disappeared into the cave and returned bearing a small box. She handed it to me.

"These earrings are for you. Wear them and may they always bring you luck."

"They're just beautiful, Maria. But you don't have to give me a gift. Keep them for one of your girls when they're older."

"I insist." She closed my hand round the box. "I want you to have them. Antonio was a good friend to me when I needed help."

She wiped a tear from her cheek with her shawl. "Go now, you'll be safe on the road to the town. The gypsies know you are friends of mine. They won't harm you."

I still have the exquisite pair of silver and coral drop earrings she gave me.

As we made our way through the cooking fires and groups of gypsies settling down for the night I looked back to wave to Maria and recalled Borrow's description of the gypsies of Sacromonte: "bronzed naked copper torsos lit by the flames, like demons".

CHAPTER FORTY-TWO

South to Gibraltar

"From Moorish cities you suddenly drop into Ramsgate."
– Théophile Gautier

One traveller said that 'waking in Granada was like waking in Paradise', but our room was stifling and the mosquitoes had done their worst.

We had only two days left before my ship was expected to reach Gibraltar, and we were keen to have time to see the Antonio Ordoñez bullfight in La Linea. So after a quick breakfast of *churros* and chocolate in the bus station, we once again hit the road for Málaga and from there to La Linea and the border with Gibraltar. Changing buses in Málaga, we just had time for a quick bowl of *gazpacho* in the bar at the bus station. It was very garlicky and thick with bread but refreshing in the gruelling afternoon heat.

Leaving Málaga and travelling westwards we passed by the village of Churriana, where Gerald Brenan spent time during the civil war, and Torremolinos, made famous by James Michener and Ernest Hemingway. The fishing villages of Fuengirola, Marbella and Estepona were unmistakable from the overpowering smell of the sardine canning factories. David pointed to the outline of Gibraltar and the coast of Africa, rising out of the shimmering heat haze. Slowly the countryside began to change as we left orange and olive trees behind in exchange for groups of fighting bulls, taking their siesta beneath the giant cork oaks. Passing through the town of San Roque, we turned towards the rock of Gibraltar and the border town of La Linea.

It was unattractive, with narrow dirty streets and a general air of poverty. But this week was their annual fair and Antonio Ordóñez was programmed to fight the next day. We headed for the bullring to check the bullfight posters. Ordóñez was the top matador of the year.

"It should be a great fight with the Miura bulls, they're really big and the bullfighters don't like them."

I was secretly hoping that our seats would be reasonably far from the ring-, my misgivings about bullfights and animal cruelty were still in my mind.

"It's incredible he invited us, very few people get to see the matador dressing," enthused David.

"Hemingway did," I reminded him.

"That's a different kettle of fish, he was writing Antonio's biography."

We decided to walk across the border into Gibraltar to save the bus fare. It was strange leaving Spain and the tricorned *Guardia Civil* border guards, and only a few yards further to see the uniformed British bobbies, and to hear them speaking a mixture of Spanish and English amongst themselves.

We crossed the airport runway and walked up Main Street in search of some cheap accommodation. At the upper end of the town we found a small *pension* in a side street. It was a relief not to have to answer the barrage of questions about our marital state that the Spanish hostelries deemed necessary. After an early supper of sausage and mash in a typical British pub, we threw ourselves on the rickety bed, exhausted from our twelve-hour journey and the relentless heat.

Too tired even to make love, we slept entwined, only waking through the night to drowsy kisses, until I was roused by unaccustomed cool air flooding through the window. A thick sea mist enveloped the rock and it seemed like a perfect day for

236

sightseeing whilst keeping cool. Refreshed by coffee and croissants, we walked to the far end of the Rock to gaze out over the Straits at Morocco and the peaks of the Rif mountains.

Like so much of Andalucía, Gibraltar was occupied by Neanderthal man. The Phoenicians visited Ceuta (Spanish Morocco) and Gibraltar, calling the two landmarks the Pillars of Hercules, using them as navigation aids through the Straits of Gibraltar. The Greeks named it Kalpe and the Arabs Yabal Tariq, or Tariq's Mountain, in honour of the Moorish General Tariq Ibn Ziyad. The Rock was alternately held by the Moors and the Christians and in 1501 troops of Queen Isabella again took control. In 1713 Spain ceded it to England and despite many attempts by them to recover it, Gibraltar has always remained in British hands. However, in the civil war, Gibraltar played its part in Spanish history again when several thousands of their citizens, both nationalists and republicans, took refuge on the Rock.

From then on, Gibraltar was a thorn in the side of the Spanish Government due to the large quantity of contraband which crossed the border. Richard Ford describes smuggling as 'the only rich, active and well-organized commercial system' in Spain. He comments that the Spanish customs agents suffer from 'official ophthalmia' and a handful of cigars ensures almost total blindness on their part.

CHAPTER FORTY-THREE

The Bullfight

"Bullfighting is the only art in which the artist is in danger of death and in which the degree of brilliance in the performance is left to the fighter's honour."
– Ernest Hemingway

In the early afternoon we crossed the border again, returning to La Linea for the bullfight, which was due to commence at five o'clock. The town had a more vibrant air than the previous day, with the *feria* crowds jostling round the bullring. Water vendors, gypsies with bunches of scarlet carnations, and country women with slices of sweet melon, all plied their wares as the band pounded out a *paso doble* at full blast.

Beautiful Spanish horses pranced by, made nervous by the music and the crowds. Their proud riders wore short black jackets, frilly white shirts, and the typical wide-brimmed cordobés hats. Behind them sat the *señoritas*, side saddle, with their hands round the rider's waist. Their polka dot flouncy dresses flipping and flowing with the movement of the horse. Carriages, pulled by gleaming black stallions, threatened to run down the mass of humanity crowding the narrow streets. The fairground was awakening from its siesta, tables and chairs set for the night's entertainment, and the ear-splitting tinny music drowning the shouts of the stall holders. The air thick with the greasy aroma of fried *churros.*

We made our way to the Hotel Mediterráneo to see Antonio, hoping he remembered his promise to give us tickets. The hotel lobby was crowded with fans hoping for a glimpse of the famous matadors. Ticket touts were everywhere, offering tickets at exorbitant prices. After all, it was the annual *feria* and Ordoñez, Puerta, and Viti were top names. We felt very important as we asked at the desk for the number of the famous man's room and told the receptionist that we were expected. We were shown into the suite by Antonio's manager.

"He's just dressing. David, you can go in, but you, *señorita*, must stay here for the moment."

I heard Antonio and David greet each other and perched myself on the only free chair in the outside room and watched, fascinated, the hustle and bustle of a bullfighter's entourage. Braces to be shortened, hair to be tied back and pink silk stockings to be straightened. Then Diego, Antonio's sword handler, called me in to the room.

"The maestro wants to see you."

Antonio, resplendent in green and gold tight trousers, kissed me as if we were long-lost friends.

"Ah, Diego, this is the *señorita* who is more concerned for the safety of the picador's horse than for mine."

Diego scowled at me. "Maestro, I am sure she wishes you a safe and successful *corrida*."

I shuffled my feet in embarrassment.

"Antonio, you know I didn't mean that. It's just that I am a horse lover."

Diego looked at his watch. "We only have half an hour before we leave, maestro, you need to get dressed."

Antonio stood before the mirror, beside a small table laid with religious and good luck charms: a crucifix, a picture of the virgin, and numerous other items he relied on to keep him safe. I had heard that bullfighters are very superstitious and that yellow is a particularly bad colour for them. Diego helped him on with the pink stockings, black slippers with bows, and tied the cords of the trousers around Antonio's calves. The braces were adjusted to ensure a snug fit. They looked very tight. Next came the white shirt and thin black tie, and finally the matching waistcoat. Antonio absent-mindedly fingered the crucifix on the table.

Diego held out the brocade jacket heavy with gold embroidery. Antonio shrugged into it and Diego settled it round his neck.

"That looks very uncomfortable," I whispered.

Antonio heard me. "It's very heavy, probably around five kilos. Have you got tickets? Diego sort them out some good tickets, as close to the ring as possible."

I was unsure that I wanted to be too close, but it was not the moment to argue.

Diego firmly evicted everyone from the room to give Antonio time to be alone with his prayers.

When he reappeared, he and his team embraced, and taking up their heavily embroidered formal capes, went down the stairs to the lobby. The level of noise increased at the sight of the famous man and his team. Autograph hunters, tourists, fans and beggars crowded round, each wanting a piece of his attention. He smiled at a pretty American girl who wished him luck and the small group pushed its way through the jostling crowd out to the big American car we had seen in Ronda.

David took my hand.

"Come on, we're going to be late. It's at least ten minutes' walk to the bullring from here."

***

Traveller William Clark wrote:

> The first question a traveller can expect on returning from Spain is, 'Have you seen a bullfight, have you encountered a bandit, or have you been present at an *auto da fe*? Since the latter two are out of fashion, a bullfight is *par excellence* the thing of Spain. So all travellers wishing to write of their experiences had to witness the spectacle, like it or not".

We joined the crush to enter the narrow stone doorway. David protected me from the mass of humanity crowding into the ring, anxious not to miss a moment of the spectacle. Just when I thought we would be trampled underfoot, we reached the steep steps leading to front rows of seats and the crowd thinned out.

We took our seats on stone benches with just enough room for short-legged spectators – David had problems manoeuvring his long legs around the buxom lady in front of him, but the holiday mood was relaxed and we all squeezed in.

"That's the box where the president sits. He usually starts the proceedings by hanging out a white handkerchief," David, a true aficionado, was really looking forward to the *corrida*.

The ring was awash with fluttering fans, and the band pounded out a well known *paso doble*. Vendors of salted almonds, peanuts, and cold water tried to make their voices heard above the din.

"Can you see the passageway round the outside of the ring?" David pointed in front of us where several *Guardia Civil* were gossiping and enjoying a cigarette. "That's called the *callejón* and it's where the bullfighters wait their turn to fight. All their assistants stand down there too."

Suddenly, I was very nervous. What if Antonio was gored? What if a horse was hurt? Would it be very bloody? I didn't want to shame David by crying. But as I looked around me I was reassured by the family groups: grandparents, parents, and children all dressed in their Sunday best, and determined to enjoy the afternoon's spectacle. Surely the children wouldn't be here if it was likely to be very gory?

The trumpets sounded and the *paseo*, procession of bullfighters, *banderilleros* and picadors on their padded horses entered the ring, to cheers from the crowd and fresh enthusiasm from the bandmaster who managed to conduct while looking over his shoulder at the spectacle in the ring. They paused at the entrance, the matadors in front, each making the sign of the cross and turning to wish luck to the group of assistants behind them.

"What do those other assistants do?" I whispered to David.

"The picadors are the men on horses. They carry a long pole with a short metal spike on the end. They are not allowed to charge the bull, but must wait until the bull attacks the horse. The picador is well padded, so it's very rare for him to be hurt. The picador's job is to weaken the bull's neck muscles so that the matador can fight the bull more easily and have more chance of a clean kill.

"The banderilleros have sticks with coloured paper and a barb on the end. They are used to excite the bull after the picadors have left the ring."

Antonio Ordóñez was stunning in his elegant green and gold *traje de luces*, his suit of lights. To roars from the crowd he and the other matadors, Diego Puerta and El Viti, walked stiff-leggedly across the ring. Behind them walked the *banderilleros* and picadors. Led by two horsemen on showy black mounts, the procession made its way to below the president's box, where they saluted him.

"Why do they wear such tight trousers and jackets? They look very difficult to run in." Though colourful, they looked impractical.

David laughed. "The idea is that the bullfighter presents a smaller target for the bull. If he had sleeves or trousers flapping it would be easier for the bull to hook him with a horn." He sighed contentedly. "This should be really good, top bullfighters and famous bulls. What a stroke of luck to meet Antonio and get these great tickets. Look, the man on the horse is asking the president for the keys to the bullpens."

The keys were thrown down, to be deftly caught by the horseman and ceremoniously handed to the keeper of the bullpens.

The ornate embroidered capes worn by the bullfighters for the procession were laid out over the railings in front of the first row, the most expensive seats. We were four rows back. Bullfighters and assistants milled around in the *callejón* and the sword handlers laid out the sheathed *estoques* the long thin swords which would be used to dispatch the bulls.

The trumpet sounded for the fight to begin.

"The most senior bullfighter goes first, so I think it will be Antonio."

My heart was in my mouth as the bull, a six hundred and twenty kilo black giant from the feared Miura ranch, hurtled into the ring. Antonio ran out alone with his pink and ochre *capote* and it seemed that the bull must surely run him through. Almost without moving his feet he played the bull with a series of *veronicas*, the cape swirling round his body, as the crowd warmed to him and with each pass a roar of *olés* rang out.

Suddenly there was a gasp from the crowd. A young man with a piece of cloth in his hand had jumped the barrier and was running towards the bull, dodging to avoid Antonio's team. The *Guardia Civil* made unenthusiastic attempts to catch him, but were obviously reluctant to enter the ring to chase the boy with such a large bull on the loose. They wisely stayed behind the barrier, leaving the job to the professionals.

"*Un espontáneo*," howled the crowd.

"What's happening, David?"

"He is a boy who wants to be a bullfighter and if he can give the bull a few good passes, he hopes to be noticed and given an opportunity. He will be arrested, but they will soon let him go."

The bull was considering this new target and digging up the sand with his front hoof.

"*Toro!*" shouted the lad, moving closer and waving the cloth.

"Let the boy fight the bull," yelled the crowd, stamping their feet. "The boy, the boy."

The bullfighters were all in the ring now, attempting to catch the young man without being gored themselves. Encouraged by the calls of the public, the boy moved closer still. The bull was biding his time.

Finally he charged and found his target. He caught the *espontáneo* under the chin and lifted him up as if he were a doll. The crowd screamed – they had wanted blood, but this was too much.

Antonio and his fellow bullfighters tried to distract the bull, and using their capes and a *banderillero* eventually managed to grab the bull by the tail. Finally, when the animal had tired of tossing the inert body of the bleeding boy, he turned his attention to the bullfighters.

My eyes were closed and I had covered my ears. I had worried about Antonio, but not expected this turn of events. David put his arm round my shoulders, as if to shield me from the scenes in the ring. The boy staggered to his feet – incredibly, he was alive.

Again screams rang out from the crowd. The bull's horn had

lifted his face off from under the chin. It was a mask of blood. He was blinded with blood and stumbling round the ring. The horrified bullfighters gasped – for what seemed like a long time, no-one moved to help him. His injuries were so horrific. The bull was watching, catching his breath, distracted by towels and capes hung over the barrier. Then Antonio's sword handler, made of sterner stuff, ran into the ring with a towel with which he covered the lad's head. Spurred on, others moved to help with the towel firmly anchored over the awful bloody mess. He was hustled past us round the *callejon* and into the bullring's hospital, escorted by the *Guardia Civil* officers.

The buzz of conversation slowly abated, and a grim and white-faced Antonio entered the ring.

"The bull is much more dangerous now," David explained me. "He knows there is a person behind the cape and will go straight for him. Antonio must kill as soon as possible."

But the fight had to run its normal course. First the picadors with their long lances to pierce the neck muscles so as to lower the bull's head. Men and horses survived this unscathed. The horses were heavy and wore thick padding. I was so relieved that they seemed to be well protected. Next the *banderilleros* danced athletically in front of the bull, placing the brightly coloured barbed sticks just behind the bulls head. Then Antonio took to the ring with his scarlet *muleta*, his cape.

There was no doubt that his intention was to kill the bull at the first opportunity. But the crowd were excited, they had tasted blood. They had paid good money and weren't about to let him short-change them. They booed and whistled until he was obliged to at least give a semblance of a normal Ordóñez performance. There was no emotion on his face. He fought the bull with grim determination. Finally, he took up the sword to end the fight. Fixing the animal's attention on the scrap of scarlet cloth he lined up for the kill. Arm raised over his head, the steel glinting in the sunlight, he drove the sword home as if his life depended on it. The bull staggered and fell to the ground. Antonio's sword had found its target and his adversary was dead.

"I've never seen a bull drop dead like that," David stood and stretched "that was incredible." Antonio was washing his hands at the side of the ring as Diego poured water from a bottle. A team of mules crossed the ring and the drovers attached the body of the bull to the traces. The crowd applauded as the mules and the bull did a circuit of the ring.

"Why are they cheering?"

"They're saluting the bravery of the bull. Do you want some water?" David waved at the man carrying big earthenware containers of chilled water.

The crowd were on their feet again, waving what looked like white cloths.

"*Oreja, oreja*," they chanted.

"Damn, I forgot my handkerchief." David rummaged in his pockets. "They want Antonio to be awarded an ear as a prize for his bravery. The top prize is the tail, then two ears and then one ear. The president is supposed to judge how many of the crowd want the matador to receive one or two ears. It's more difficult to win an ear in a big important bullring like this one, than in a small village fight."

I was exhausted with nervous tension. Only another five bulls to go.

Whilst in later years I became an *aficionada* of the bullfight I have to agree with Michener that the first fight one sees is:

> usually an unrewarding experience, a confusing spectacle in which the bull appears only as a necessary and fractious evil who, after disrupting everyone's plans, ends ignominiously as a kind of animated pincushion. But when one has attended many *corridas* and begun to catch a glimmer of the intricate and subtle construction of a bullfight, [he] begins to centre his attention on the animal and occasionally he will sense the overtones of the tremendous drama being enacted before him: the confrontation of man and primordial animal.

In Hemingway's opinion the repressed sensuality of the Spanish is released by the spectacle of the bullfight, and several other writers have pronounced that the violence of Spanish bandits is due to becoming accustomed to the violence of the bullfight from an early age.

My recollection of that, my first bullfight, was that I was completely drained – mentally and physically. The drama, the danger, the blood of the bull and the boy, the terror that a horse might be harmed (which it was not), the noise and the colour, and the elegance and courage of Ordóñez between the enormous bull's horns, was an assault on the senses. I left the ring that evening confused and feeling as a Roman might after his first afternoon at the Coliseum, watching Christians massacre lions, or vice versa. For the Spaniard, the point of the bullfight is the nobility of death – the Moment of Truth that comes to us all. The matador is graceful, proud and calm. He must be respectful to the bull and its death must be noble.

"What did you think?" asked David. "It was just great, wasn't it?" He looked with surprise at my pale and exhausted face.

"What's the matter?"

"I just don't know what I feel. I'm confused. It's so unexpected and so unlike anything else I have ever experienced. I need time to think about it."

He put his arm round my shoulders, "Let's go back to the hotel. It's probably our last night together."

I didn't want to be reminded of how little time we had left.

We left the bullring and walked through the still vibrant fair towards the border, silent from what we had just witnessed, and jostled by touts and children offering contraband watches, cigarettes and sweets.

***

The following day David travelled back to Spain as planned to complete some drawings of fighting bulls. He was to be there for a day and might stay overnight, before returning to Gibraltar for his flight to England. I had enquired at the shipping office when the S. S. Orantes was likely to arrive as it had been delayed on its journey back from Australia. It seemed fate might give us one more night together if there was a further delay When he left I mooched up and down Main Street, jostled by visitors from cruise ships buying tacky watches and perfumes. Mr Bulshand's emporium was an Aladdin's cave of bacon, fresh butter, and sausages – items unavailable in the inland villages of Andalucía.

Late in the afternoon I visited the shipping office again.

"I have good news, Miss Jill," the Indian clerk beamed. "The ship will be here tonight without fail, departing tomorrow morning."

My heart sank – that was not good news as I would probably not see David again until we were both back in England.

Disconsolately, I sat on a bench at the bottom of Main Street and read a crumpled copy of yesterday's newspaper. Suddenly I saw his familiar figure swinging up the street, with his shaggy mop of unruly hair, worn out jeans and brilliant smile.

"I had to see you before you went."

He dropped his bag and taking my face in both hands, kissed me hard.

"I came back early just for you. Aren't you flattered?"

Flattered? I was so in love my heart was dancing a *paso doble*.

We sat on a bench outside a pub, watching the sun set over the Ronda mountains.

"It seems ages since we were in Ronda." I leaned my head on his shoulder. "Do you realize we haven't made plans to meet up when we get home? It's alright for you, you've got a job. But I'm broke."

David stood up and slung his bag over his shoulder. "We'll try and find you something not too far away from my stables. Relax, let's enjoy the time we have left."

We made good use of those unexpected hours in our steamy little room at the *pension*, making love greedily far into the night.

Early next morning he came with me to the quayside.

"I'll miss you so much, call me as soon as you get back," I begged him, hugging him tightly.

He turned my face up to his and kissed me tenderly.

"Just you try and get rid of me. And keep away from those good-looking sailors."

I laughed and joined the crowds waving farewell from the rail as the ship as she pulled out into the Bay of Algeciras, and I waved until my arm ached and the morning sea mist hid him from view.

***

I never saw him again. They said he lost control of the car. They said he died instantly.

I had lost my love. But my love affair with Spain had just begun.

EPILOGUE

It was a warm December afternoon. The train from Madrid had, for once, arrived in Málaga on time. Leaning out of the window, I breathed in the familiar smells of Spain. I searched for a familiar figure on the platform.

A tall, bronzed young man in the uniform of the Spanish Army strolled casually through the jostling crowds, deftly avoiding the porters with laden trolleys who threatened to run him down. Beside him loped a large German shepherd.

"Vicente, I've missed you. You got my telegram."

As I moved to kiss him a quiet growl from the dog stopped me. Yellow eyes looked up at me and warned me that he was spoken for.

"Who's this?"

"This is Tara, she's the love of my life."

"Can we share you?"

"Ask Tara. She's always been faithful. You promised you'd be back in ten days and it's taken you four months."

"It's a long story. I'll tell you one day."

He picked up my case.

"*Dios*, that's heavy. How long are you staying?"

"It appears that depends on Tara. I'll stay as long as you'll both have me."

Superstitions

Andalucían folklore is rich in superstitions. Many come from the gypsy culture, and each village seems to create its own beliefs. These are some that I came across:

It is bad luck to build a staircase on the left of the entrance door.

Shoes on a table, wine on a bed, or open scissors bring bad luck

When cats play it will rain.

A fisherman must enter the boat with his right foot.

A plait in a horse's mane avoids the evil eye.

If you spill wine on a tablecloth, it brings good luck, but only if you wet your finger in the wine and make the sign of the cross on your forehead.

A sprig of rosemary in your hat keeps witches away

Always cut your nails on a Friday to avoid toothache.

Never count the stars, or you will get that number of wrinkles on your face (or spots on your hands).

When a single person has his foot touched with a broom the possibility of marriage is brushed away.

When a dog howls close to an ill person he announces his death and if he digs in the same place three days in a row a grave is being dug.

To avoid the soul of the dead coming back to haunt you, you must kiss the shoes the deceased will be buried in.

To know if a woman will give birth to a boy or a girl, see which foot she normally goes upstairs with. Right means a boy, left a girl.

Never walk on spilt salt, and if you spill oil you must sprinkle salt on it in the form of a cross.

If the cock crows at a strange time it will rain. If he crows four times before midnight he announces death.

The end of your bed should not face the door or you will die before moving house.

Snakes are friendly to men but not to women and lizards are friendly to women but enemies of men.

In a marriage, the partner with the smallest ears dies first.

To get rid of unwanted guests stand a broom or a shoe behind the door, or put salt on the fire.

If you count ten stars on ten successive nights before the feast of San Juan (23rd June) you will dream of your future husband.

Girls named Maria bring luck and they can remove the evil eye.

Never touch the wax of a candle.

If nine male children are born in succession to a family, the ninth has special grace and healing powers.

If a black bird sits on a roof it is because a man is dying.

Rooks abandon their nests at an approaching death and do not return until after the funeral.

If you dream of nursing a crying baby, you or a close relative will die.

Gerald Brenan wrote of his experience in Yegen in the Alpujarras. When walking in a valley in the mountains, he stopped to drink from a stream and became aware of movement – a large grey animal which he thought was a wolf or a dog was staring fixedly at him. On his return home he mentioned this to his servant who said:

"Did you ask what it wanted?"

"No," said Brenan "it was a wild animal."

"Yes" answered the servant. "It may have seemed to be just an animal but we believe that souls who cannot find rest return as animals who wander until they can reveal to someone what is troubling them."

The traditional witch on a broomstick with a pointed hat – a *bruja* – was out of fashion in many villages, and had been supplanted by the *hechicera*, hairy flying witches. They no longer flew through the air on a broomstick but were said to use a spinning wheel on their heads, and to fly with their skirts hitched up. According to Brenan, the height of the village influenced the quality of the witchcraft and the village of Trevélez, high in the Alpujarras, was renowned for its hams over which the resident witches had cast spells. One young girl was said to have the power to turn her boyfriend into a donkey, enabling her to ride him through the sky.

Some of my Favourite Books on the History of Spain

A Spanish Labyrinth, Gerald Brenan, 1990
Modern Spain 1875-1980, Raymond Carr, 2001
Ferdinand and Isabella, J. Edwards, 2004
A New International History of the Spanish Civil War,
Michael Alpert, 2004
Catherine of Aragon, Giles Tremlett, 2010
Juan Carlos: A People's King, Paul Preston, 2004
The Spanish Holocaust, Paul Preston, 2011

Some of my Favourite General Books on Spain

Live and Work in Spain, Guy Hobbs
Mad Dogs and an English Girl, , Caroline Waterman
Spain By the Horns, Tim Elliott
The Lemon Trilogy, Chris Stewart
The Return, Victoria Hislop

Bibliography

A Guide to Spain, Shea The Tagus and the Tiber, W. F. Baxter

A Handbook for Travellers in Spain, Richard Ford

A Scamper in Spain, A.C. Andros

A Summer in Andalucia, George Dennis

A Summer in Spain, C.H. Ramsay

Apuntes para Antropologia Andaluza, Augustin Garcia Chicon

Arriate, Cronicas de un Pueblo del Siglo XX

Babel in Spain, John Haycroft.

Bandoleros y Asesinos en Malaga, Diego Ceano

Benjamin Disraeli in Spain, Donald Sultana

Castile and Andalucia, Louisa Tenison

Cities and Wilds of Andalucia, Dundas Murray

Costumbres Andaluzas, Jose Maria de Mena

Crime on the Road Malaga to Almeria, Norman Bethune

Cronica Municipal de Arriate, Juan Antonio Marquez

Don Gypsy, Walter Starkie

El Decreto de la Alhambra, David Raphael

El Folklore Andaluz, Antonio Mechado y Alvarez

Excursions in the Mountains of Ronda, Rochfort Scott

Expulsion de los Judios de España, Valeriu Marcu

Gatherings in Spain, Richard Ford

Historia de El Burgo, Jose Maria Gomez

Historias Leyendas, Tradiciones y Folklore en el Valle del Guadalhorce, Antonio Saez Lopez, Ayunt. De Alhaurin de la Torre y Fco, Doña Doña

History of Protestantism, Dr Wylie

Homage to Catalonia, George Orwell

La Andalucia de los libros de Viajes del Siglo XIX, Manuel Bernal Rodriguez

Las Aves de la Serrania de Ronda, Juan Oñate Garcia

Letters from Spain, John Leycester Adolphus

Malaga a Mes y Mantel, Enrique Capelli

Malaga en la Leyenda, Mateo Gallego y Fco Lancha

Notes on Spain, Edwin Lee

Poem on Black Douglas, John Barbour

Portrait of Spain, Thomas McGann

Recollections of Spanish Travel, Penelope Holland

Sketches in Spain, Samuel Cook

Summer Months in Spain or Gazpacho, William George Clark

Sunny Spain, Olive Patch

The Bible in Spain and The Zincali, George Borrow

The Bridle Roads of Spain, George Cayley

The Spanish Civil War, Helen Graham

Two Middle Aged Ladies in Andalusia, Penelope Chetwode

Viajeros Britanicos en Malaga, Krauel

Virgin Spain, The Drama of a Great People, Waldo Frank

Wanderings in Spain, Augustus John Cuthbert Hare

Important Dates in the History of Spain

20.000-16.000 BC (approx) Paelolithic Age
800 BC Phoenician invasion Foundation of Cadiz
575 BC Greek invasion Foundation of Ampurias
228 BC Carthaginian invasion
218 BC Second Punic War Hannibal invades Italy, Romans invade Spain
45 BC Julius Caesar wins Battle of Munda
417 Visigoths fight under Roman flag
456 Visigoths invade Spain and occupy the south and centre of country
507 French overcome the Visigoths
681 Anti Jewish legislation passed
694 Jews sold into slavery
711 Arab/Moorish invasion
756 Abd al-Rahman I founds Omeyan emirate of Cordoba
929 Abd al-Rahman III proclaimed caliph of Cordoba
1031 End of reign of the caliphs and takeover of Taifas
1043 Birth of El Cid
1094 El Cid named Governor of Valencia
1099 Death of El Cid
1148 Almohades conquer Al Andalus
1173 End of Almohades supremacy
1391 Wave of Anti Jewish progroms
1469 Marriage of King Fernando and Queen Isabella
1473 Slaughter of conversos in Andalucia (Jews converted to Christianity)
1478 Creation of Spanish Inquisition
1492 Granada taken by Fernando and Isabella from

the Moors. Jews exiled. Columbus discovers America.

1502 Muslims ordered to convert or go into exile.

1588 Spanish Armada loses to the English fleet

1605 Don Quijote published

1609 All moriscos exiled (Moors converted to Christianity)

1704 English fleet takes Gibraltar

1789 Goya named Royal Painter

1805 Battle of Trafalgar English destroy French and Spanish fleets at Cadiz

1808 Spanish War of Independence against Napoleon. Joseph Bonaparte Crowned King of Spain

1812 Constitution declared in Cadiz

1873 First Republic declared

1931 Second Republic declared

1936 Spanish Civil War breaks out. International Brigades arrive in Madrid.

1939 End of Spanish Civil War, period of extreme repression commences

1940 Spain declares itself a non combatant in the Second World War.